HEINEMANN
TEXT PROCESSING
for modular awards

MEDICAL WORD PROCESSING

STAGE II

GW00418683

BARBARA EDWARDS

Heinemann

Heinemann Educational Publishers,
Halley Court, Jordan Hill, Oxford OX2 8EJ
A division of Reed Educational & Professional Publishing Ltd

Heinemann is a registered trademark of Reed Educational & Professional Publishing
Limited

OXFORD MELBOURNE AUCKLAND
JOHANNESBURG BLANTYRE GABORONE
IBADAN PORTSMOUTH NH (USA) CHICAGO

First published 1998
2002 2001 2000 99 98
10 9 8 7 6 5 4 3 2 1

A catalogue record for this book is available from the British Library on request.

ISBN 0 435 45392 0

Designed by Jackie Hill

Typeset by TechType, Abingdon, Oxon

Printed and bound in Great Britain by Athenaeum Press Ltd, Gateshead, Tyne & Wear

Acknowledgements

I would like to thank Rosalyn Bass and Natasha Goddard at Heinemann Educational
for their help and assistance in the production of this book. I would also like to thank
my husband, Arthur, for his endless keying in, proofreading and patience.

Barbara Edwards

Contents

About this book

This book provides coverage of the RSA Medical Word Processing Part 2 examination. It is anticipated that users of this book will have achieved or be working towards the RSA Stage II Text Processing Part 1 and RSA Stage II Word Processing Part 2 awards.

The vocabulary used for explanations is kept as simple as possible.

The book is divided into three sections:

■ 1   General Theory

This section provides information on special requirements for working in the medical environment and also for the examination itself.

■ 2   Exercises

This section is divided into two parts: Health Centre and Hospital. In the first, you will take the part of a junior medical secretary working at the Liberty Health Centre in Wells, near Bath. As you work through these exercises you will be concerned with an open afternoon on First Aid and a Health Checks Clinic. In the second part, you will take the part of a medical secretary working at the Quantock District Hospital in Taunton. As you progress through the exercises you will work in four different departments, namely cardiology; orthopaedic and physiotherapy; gynaecology; and otorhinolaryngology. All the exercises will provide you with practice in keying in the different types of document that you are likely to come across in the medical environment.

■ 3   Exam Practice

This section provides you with 5 mock examination papers as well as hints and tips for sitting the examination.

■ Format of the book

The exercises in this book are handwritten as well as typewritten. This type of presentation is practised in the examination as well as in the workplace. Some of the tasks may be more demanding than those you will meet in the examinations. This will help you to develop your confidence and ability to succeed in the examination, as well as preparing you for working in the medical environment.

Some of the exercises include draft documents which may have some incorrely spelt words which you will be asked to change when the document is recalled.

Letterheads for use with the exercises throughout this book can be found at the back of the book on page 118. You may photocopy these for use with this book. Alternatively, your tutor may provide you with templates for the letterheads.

Worked examples for all the mock examination papers are included at the end of the book on pages 103–117. They have been reduced in size to A6.

House style

Each employer in the medical profession will have its own particular style and methods of laying out documents. The standard referral letters in this book are fully blocked, ie. each new paragraph should start at the left-hand side.

If there is an enclosure or enclosures to be sent with a letter, the abbreviation *Enc* or *Encs* is typed two spaces below the last line.

When an extra copy of a letter has to be sent, the abbreviation *cc* should be added, together with any routing information two spaces below the enclosure abbreviation or last line (eg. cc X-Ray Department). An original and two copies of the letter should be printed (or two photocopies of the original made), and a tick placed after the appropriate entry on each copy. The third copy will be the file copy. The following example shows how each copy would be marked.

Original
Encs

cc   X-Ray Department
      File

Copy 1
Encs

cc   X-Ray Department ✔
      File

Copy 2
Encs

cc   X-Ray Department
      File ✔

General Theory

■ Introduction to medical terminology

As you work through this book, and certainly if you obtain employment in a medical office, you will meet many new words and phrases. It would be a good idea to invest in a medical dictionary and/or dictionary of nursing. These are printed by specialist medical publishers and a good bookshop should have a copy or be able to order one for you.

If you are employed in a medical office and using a word processor, then you may find that many of these medical words and terms have been added to the dictionary on the software. This will almost certainly be the case if you are using a computer that is linked to a network. If you are using a stand-alone computer, then the previous job holder may have done this for you. Whichever is the case, as you come across new words, you should add them to the dictionary to help you in the future. Before doing this, check with your supervisor, or if you are at college, ask your tutor for advice.

If you are working for a GP or GPs in a health centre, you will soon become familiar with a wide range of medical vocabulary. If you are a secretary working in a large hospital, you may find yourself in a specialist department and become very knowledgeable about this aspect of medical work. Some typical medical departments may include:

Department	Deals with matters concerning the study, diagnosis or treatment of:
Anaesthetics	the loss of feeling
Cardiology	the heart
Dermatology	skin disorders
Endocrinology	glands and hormones
Forensic medicine	the causes of injury and death in unexplained circumstances
Gastroenterology	digestive tract, liver, biliary tract and pancreas
General surgery	injuries, deformities or disease by operation or manipulation
Gynaecology	the female reproductive system
Haematology	the blood
Intensive therapy unit	seriously ill patients by specialist care
Medicine	disease or injury by drugs
Neurology	the nervous system
Obstetrics	pregnancy and childbirth
Oncology	tumours
Orthopaedic	deformities caused by disease or damage to the bones and joints of the skeleton
Otorhinolaryngology	ear, nose and throat (ENT)
Paediatrics	childhood ailments

Pathology	the disease process, nature and causes
Physiotherapy	healing by exercise including the use of infrared, and ultraviolet rays, etc
Psychiatry	mental disorders
Radiology	disease or injury by X-Ray
Reconstructive surgery	damaged or deformed parts of the body by plastic surgery
Respiratory	breathing
Urology	the urinary tract

To help you to build up your medical vocabulary, keep a notebook and add new words and phrases as you meet them. If there is something you do not understand, ask your supervisor, or the person who gave you the task to complete, to explain.

Keying in medical text

Over the years, it has become traditional to set out documents in certain ways, but the important point is to ensure that your documents are clear to the reader. It is difficult to give specific rules for setting out tasks as each doctor or consultant will adopt his or her own way of doing things. Be aware of different ways of setting things out and be prepared to adapt to suit the preferred methods of your employer. It is essential to be *consistent* within a document. Aim to do this within each document in this book and you will be well-prepared for your examination.

Line spacing

Double-line spacing is often used to help all concerned to read and understand the document. It is also used when producing a draft of a document to allow space for amendments to be made by hand.

Emphasising text

■ Spaced capitals

Some words are emphasised in documents by spaced capitals. The following is an example.

C A R D I O L O G Y   D E P A R T M E N T

To key in spaced capitals:

- tap the space bar once between each letter, *and*
- three times between each word.

If the words occur in the middle of a sentence:

- leave three spaces before the words in spaced capitals, and after the words *and*
- three spaces after them.

Note: when you are using a word processor spaced capitals may not always look clear when you print your work – it will depend on the type of font you are using.

■ Capitals

Some words are emphasised in documents by closed capitals. The following is an example.

ORTORHINOLARYNGOLOGY DEPARTMENT

To key in closed capitals, depress the caps lock. Initial capitals may also be used, but they should be used with underscore as shown below.

<u>Yoga Exercise Class</u>

■ Emboldening and underlining

Words or phrases may be emboldened or underlined as shown in the following examples.

WELL WOMAN CLINIC

<u>FIRST AID COURSE</u>

In the examination, you may be asked to emphasise a word or heading. In this case, you may choose which method to use. Italic, as shown below, is an acceptable alternative.

GYNAECOLOGY DEPARTMENT

You may also use a combination of more than one style.

In this book, follow the style given in the draft material.

Punctuation

There are no special requirements for punctuation within medical documents. The normal practice is to leave two spaces at the end of a sentence after a full stop, a question mark or an exclamation mark – although one space is also acceptable. Within a sentence, punctuation such as a comma, a colon or semi-colon is followed by one space. It is essential to be consistent.

Continuation sheets

There are no special ways of producing continuation sheets for medical documents. The normal way is to begin numbering with page 2. The number is keyed in as a figure and may be placed at the top or bottom of each continuation sheet.

Security and confidentiality when working in a medical office

When you start work, you will be asked to sign a Contract of Employment. This must be provided by all employers, and will almost certainly contain a section that refers to confidentiality. This will ask you to agree not to disclose any confidential information about your employer, the medical office in which you will be working, or the details of any patients. This confidentiality will extend even after you have left your particular employment.

Always make sure you follow good office practice.

- Do not leave papers and folders lying around.
- Put items away when not in use.
- Use screen savers or switch to a blank document when visitors are around.
- Shred any spoilt sheets.

You will have your own personal password to allow you to use your computer or to access the network. This password should not be disclosed to anyone else. The doctor or practice manager for whom you are working will be able to access documents via his or her own password.

Medical documentation has to be stored for many years. Special, long-term storage facilities may be provided, and buildings and storage rooms should be dry and well-ventilated.

Abbreviations

There are no abbreviations used in the RSA Medical Word Processing Stage II examination. In this book, where an abbreviation appears, there will always be an instruction asking you to retain the abbreviation.

Correction signs

When you see the following signs you must carry out the instructions.

New paragraph	// or ⌊	Start a new paragraph
Run on		Continue to type on the same line, ignore the paragraph break.
Insertion		Insert the circled words exactly where the insertion sign points – be careful to note where any punctuation may be. For example, you may have to insert a number of words before a comma or full stop that is already on the page – make sure you don't forget to include it.
Transpose horizontally *or balloon with arrow*		Move the words around so that the last section becomes the first word to type.
Transpose vertically		This means you have to change the line on which the words/figures are typed. Remember to look at the arrows carefully – you should only move text that is directly covered by the arrows.
Close up		This means you should remove any extra spaces.
Leave a space	/	Leave a space wherever this sign appears.

stet

in the margin:

This means that you should type only the words that have a dotted line underneath them.

1

◼ Proofreading your work

It is very important to check your finished work thoroughly. Accuracy faults are the most likely faults to prevent success in any word processing examination. In the workplace, it is vital to be accurate in your work, particularly in a medical office. Inaccuracy can lead to serious consequences, especially when you are keying in difficult medical terminology and the names of drugs.

To improve your accuracy, always use the correct fingering when keying in work. This will allow you to concentrate on the rough script in front of you, and to follow any instructions. When you have finished keying in a task, always read the work on screen, and use the spellchecker. It will find misspelt words and keying errors, but it will not find wrong words that are spelt correctly (eg 'their' instead of 'there').

A final check should be carried out against the rough script (or examination paper) when you have printed your work. Note any errors on the printed copy using a pen or pencil, recall the document to screen, make the corrections and then reprint.

Read the following three documents carefully and try to find all the errors. When you think you have found them all, check your answers against the key at the back of the book (pages 101–2).

Proofreading Exercise 1

The Treatment Of Varicose Veins

The most commonly effected veins are the saphenous (superficial) veins of the legs. There is an inherited tendency to varicose veins, but obstruction to blood flow is responsible in some cases. Complications can occur such as thrombosis phlebitis and haemorhage. Treatment includes elastic support, stripping or in some cases excision .

there are various grades of elastic support available, from those designed for early varicose veins through to those for pa6ients with really severe problems. The elastic support is designed to improve circulation, ease the discomfort or pain and in severe cases conceal blemishes. Supports come in different hosiery styles and include thigh, open toad thigh, below knee and open toe below knee. There are also support hose available formen which are indistinguishable from normal socks,

Proofreading Exercise 2

REGAINING CONTROL OF YOUR BLADDER

In britain today there are about 3 million poeple of all ages who have lost some control over when and where they pass urine. This condition is known as incontinence. There are two types of incontinence, stress and urge.

If your leakage from the blasser occurs when sneezing. coughing or exercising, this is stress incontinence. The leakage, which may even occur when walking, is caused by a weakening of the bladder out let and pelvic floor muscles. It can affect women of all ages.

patients who suffer a sudden need to pass urine but are unable to reach the toilet in time are suffering from urge incontinence. They may also need to pass u8rine more often than usual and may have to get up several times in the night. Bed-wetting is also a symptum. This condition is often caused by an overactive or unstable bladder, and tends to happen as people get older. There is often less warning and the bladder needs emptying more often.

An overactive bladder may be trained at home by suppressing the contractions. This is done by gradually increasing the capacity of the bladder and the time interval between passing water. If a patient experiences difficulty when trying to do this, they may find the following suggestions helpful:

1   make a drink
2   sit on the feet
3   cross the legs
4   sit on a rolled up towel

It is important for patients to keep up fluid intake of 8-12 cups a day, andto continue with pelvic floor exercises.

Proofreading Exercise 3

Registration No: R 9701969

date of keying-in

Mrs Edwina Barber
        57 White Horse Road
Westbury
Wilts
BA12 8LE

Dear Mrs Barber

The following appointment has been made for you to see

MR L JUCK, CONSULTANT OPHTHALMOLOGIST
at WARMINSTER HOSPITAL

Appointment: (insert date for second Thursday, 2-months time) at 10.15 am

On arrival please report to the Reception Disk which is at the main entrance and you will be directed to the out-patient waiting area.

transport has not been arranged for this appointment unless otherwise stated. should you require transport it is neceSsary for you to contact your GP who will arrange this for you.

Please bring detials of your current medication.

IT IS ADVICED BY THE CONSULTENT THAT YOU DO NOT DRIVE YOURSELF TO THE CLINIC, AS IT MAY BE NECESSARY TO PUT DROPS INTO YOUR EYES WHICH MAY BLUR YOUR VISION.

IF YOU CANNOT KEEP THIS APPOINTMENT IT IS IMPORTANT THAT YOU PHONE MR LUCK'S SECRETARY ON 01985 123456 AS SOON AS POSSIBLE, SO THAT THIS APOINTMENT CAN BE OFFERED TO ANOTHER PATIENT.

Yours sincerely

E M MEDLAR (Mrs)
MEDICAL SECRETARY

Exercises

 ## Health Centre Exercises

A health centre has a number of doctors in general practice who run their own surgeries as well as visiting the chronically sick in their own homes. Often each of the doctors specialises in a different branch of medicine, and patients are seen at the surgery on an appointments system. Nursing staff are in attendance to run the baby clinics, well woman and HRT (Hormone Replacement Therapy) clinics and assist the doctors with blood tests, injections, and general health checks, etc.

If you are working in a health centre you may be asked to complete tasks for any of the doctors and nursing staff in the practice. The work will include

- general correspondence, including letters of medical referral
- memoranda
- reports
- circulars
- notices
- maintaining appointments systems
- preparing visiting lists
- preparing rotas
- arranging locum cover.

First Aid

First aid is the treatment given to a patient who suffers an injury or sudden illness before the arrival of professional medical personnel, or admission to hospital. Most first-aid treatment deals with sprains, cuts, minor burns and other minor injuries, and demands proficiency in the application of bandages, splints and dressings. Emergency first aid is designed to protect the patient from further injury, to reassure the patient and family, to prevent the condition from getting worse, to aid recovery and to preserve life.

Your tasks for this department are concerned with the Open Afternoon on First Aid.

In the course of your work in this department, you may come across some medical terms which you are not familiar with. These are listed below. If there are any other words which you do not understand, look them up in a dictionary.

allergy (allergic)	adverse reaction of the body to a substance
anaphylactic shock	major allergic reaction within the body which may lead to a person's collapse
anticoagulants	drugs that prevent the clotting of blood – used to stop blood clots forming or to break up blood clots
blister	swelling containing serum (a clear, yellowish fluid)
blood pressure	pressure of blood against the walls of the main arteries; normal range varies with age
clot	semi-solid blood (when blood turns from a liquid into a solid)
compress	pad of material soaked in hot or cold water
diagnosis	process of determining a disease by considering signs and symptoms, etc
resuscitation	involves maintaining the flow of blood to the body's organs until the person's heartbeat and breathing can be restarted
rupture	bursting apart of an organ or tissue
sterile	completely free from bacteria, etc
tissues	collection of cells from which the body is built
vessels	tubes carrying body fluid, especially blood

First Aid Exercise 1

Please type this with a justified right margin

A BRIEF INSIGHT

TREATING MINOR INJURIES

Insert FIRST AID to appear as a header on every page

Leave at least 50mm here

Every casualty needs to feel secure and in safe hands. You will need to be able to give an air of calmness and confidence to the casualty. Speak gently but be firm when explaining what you are going to do. Reassure the casualty when you have completed your treatment. Hold their hands, keep their trust in you and never let them feel alone.

Copy this paragraph to ⒶⒷ

Most first aid is practical common sense which you can teach yourself. It is the assistance or treatment given to someone injured or suddenly taken ill before the arrival of an ambulance, doctor or other qualified person.

Among the common forms of accident in the house or personal injuries are a number of everyday incidents. Nose bleeding occurs when blood vessels inside the nostrils are ruptured. This can happen from blowing, picking, sneezing or a blow to the nose. Blood pressure is another reason for a nose bleed to occur. Having a cold or flu infection can cause the blood vessels in the nose to become fragile and this in turn can contribute to a nose bleed. ~~Applying pressure to~~ *Pinching* the fleshy part of the nose for about 10 minutes usually allows the blood to clot.

Summer picnics are often marred by stings. Bee, wasp or hornet stings are usually painful ~~but not really~~ *rather than* dangerous. Some people are allergic to stings and can *quickly* develop anaphylactic shock. Stings in the mouth can be serious as they can obstruct the airway. If the sting is still in the wound, pluck it out with fine tweezers and apply a cold compress to relieve the pain and minimise the swelling.

Minor burns and scalds (superficial burns) are often caused by accidents in the ~~home~~ *house*. ⊘ Blisters usually form on the skin that has been damaged by heat or friction. During healing new skin forms at the base of the blister. ⌐

This is why it is important never to break a blister.

Cool the injured skin with plenty of cold water to stop the burning and relieve the pain. Cover with a sterile dressing and bandage loosely in place.

Ⓐ

You feel a sharp pain followed by swelling and ~~soreness~~ *usually*

This is a draft. Make sure you save it

First Aid Exercise 2

The Liberty Health Centre *Emphasise this heading*

→OPEN AFTERNOON FIRST AID

We shall be holding an Open Afternoon in August when members from three Voluntary Aid Societies will be giving demonstrations on actions to be taken in emergencies.

These demonstrations will include the following.

Assessing a burn
Initial assessment
Dressings
Manual moves
Making a diagnosis
Treatment and aftercare
Recovery position
Resuscitation

During the afternoon you can discuss details of the courses run. You can learn about caring services in support of community needs, as well as caring for people in crisis both at home and abroad.

Miss Jane Adams
The Liberty Health Centre
The Liberty
WELLS
BA5 2FX

This is a draft. Make sure you save it.

First Aid Exercise 3

THE LIBERAL HEALTH CENTRE

> Check the name of the Health Centre from **Exercise 2** and amend if necessary

It is very important to ensure that sufficient quantities of the most used items are kept in stock.

BASIC FIRST AID MATERIALS	STORAGE DRAWER	STOCK DETAILS	
		ORDERING CODE	MINIMUM REQUIREMEN
Dressings			
Adhesive dressings	Top left	ABB1	20
Fabric plaster	Top left	ABC2	6
Waterproof plaster	Top left	ABD3	6
Clear plaster	Top left	ABE 4	6
Sterile dressing	Top left	ABF S	2
Finger plaster	Top left	ABG 6	2
Bandages			
Crepe roller	Top right	BCC1	1
Open weave roller	Top right	BCD 2	1
Finger gauze	Top right	BCE 3	1
Elasticated roller	Top right	BCF 4	1
Self-adhesive roller	Top right	BCG S	1
Useful items			
Disposable gloves	Bottom right	CDC 2	1 pair
Scissors	Middle right	CDD 4	1
Tweezers	Middle right	CDE 6	1
Cotton Wool	Middle left	CDF S	1 roll
Pins and clips	Middle right	CDG 3	1 pack
Wound cleaning wipes	Middle left	CDH 1	1 pack

> Please sort into exact ordering code number within each section. Ensure that all corresponding details are also re-arranged

> Please modify layout so that Dressings follow Bandages

> Please move Minimum Requirement column to come before Ordering Code column

First Aid Exercise 4

(Insert Ⓐ from following page.)

Dear Mr Riley

Re Open Afternoon
   First Aid Demonstration

We would like to invite you and the members of your Youth Club to come along to the above Open Afternoon. We are sure it will be of interest to all the young people. Basic first aid cannot be taught at too early an age.

There will be demonstrations by representatives from the three local Voluntary Aid Societies and they will have volunteers on hand to give more details on the courses they run and the qualifications that can be gained.

The demonstrations will include: how to make an initial assessment of an injury and how to summon appropriate help if necessary; what dressings to use; how to put a patient in the recovery position; and many others, demonstrations through to aftercare help for the patient and/or relatives.

Volunteers will be needed to take part in these demonstrations and I am sure this will appeal to some of the young people from your Youth Club.

(Insert Ⓑ from following page.)

Yours sincerely

Jane Adams

(Top + 2 please.
One file copy and
one for Practice Manager.
Indicate routing.)

Extra Text for Exercise 4

Ⓐ JA/your initials
Mr J Riley
Mendip View Youth Club
Holly Cottage
East Horrington
WELLS
BA5 4SJ

Ⓑ Free ~~drinks~~ ~~refreshments~~ will be served during the afternoon. To assist with the catering arrangements I ~~should~~ would be grateful if you ~~could~~ would let me know ~~on~~ the approximate number of people who will be ~~able to join us~~ joining us.

First Aid Exercise 5

Open the document you saved in Exercise 2 and make the following changes.

The Liberty Health Centre

FIRST AID OPEN AFTERNOON

We shall be holding an Open Afternoon in ~~August~~ July when members from three Voluntary Aid Societies will be giving demonstrations on actions to be taken in emergencies.

These demonstrations will include the following.

Assessing a burn
Initial assessment
Dressings
Manual moves
Making a diagnosis
Treatment and aftercare
Recovery position
Resuscitation

Sort into exact alphabetical order and indent 25 mm from the left margin.

During the afternoon you can discuss further details of the courses run. You can learn about caring services in support of community needs, as well as caring for people in crisis both at home and abroad.

and qualifications to be obtained from the Aid Societies.

Centre this section

Miss Jane Adams
The Liberty Health Centre
The Liberty
WELLS
BA5 2FX
01749 123456

Find out more about how first aid can save a life in an emergency. Come along and join us at the Health Centre grounds. For further details contact:

First Aid Exercise 6

Open the document you saved in Exercise 1 and make the amends below

FIRST AID

Change to double-line spacing please

2

TREATING MINOR INJURIES

A BRIEF INSIGHT

It is particularly important when dealing with young children to gain the child's confidence.

Move this paragraph to (A)

Every casualty needs to feel secure and in safe hands. You will need to be able to give an air of calmness and confidence to the casualty. Speak gently but be firm when explaining what you are going to do. Reassure the casualty when you have completed your treatment. Hold their hands, keep their trust in you and never let them feel alone.

Most first aid is practical common sense which you can teach yourself. It is the assistance or treatment given to someone injured or suddenly taken ill before the arrival of an ambulance, doctor or other qualified person.

(A)

home

Among the common forms of accident in the ~~house~~ or personal injuries are a number of everyday incidents. Nose bleeding occurs when blood vessels inside the nostrils are ruptured. This can happen from blowing,

from

picking, sneezing or a blow to the nose. Blood pressure is another reason for a nose bleed to occur. Having a cold or flu infection can cause the blood vessels in the nose to become fragile and this in turn can contribute to a nose bleed. Pinching the fleshy part of the nose for about 10 minutes usually allows the blood to clot.

This paragraph only in single line spacing

Internal bleeding seeping through the tissues can cause bruising. Some bruises develop slowly over a few days and others appear rapidly. The elderly and those on anticoagulants can bruise easily.

To treat the bruise, raise and support the injured part in a comfortable position. Apply a cold compress to the area. Some people use a pack of frozen vegetables, usually peas, for this but do remember to wrap the pack in a cloth before applying it to the skin.

First Aid Exercise 6 continued

FIRST AID

Summer picnics are often marred by stings. Bee, wasp or hornet stings
are usually painful rather than dangerous. You usually feel a sharp pain
followed by swelling and soreness. Some people are allergic to stings
and can quickly develop anaphylactic shock. Stings in the mouth can be
serious as they can obstruct the airway. [If the sting is still in the wound,
pluck it out with fine tweezers and apply a cold compress to relieve the
pain and minimise the swelling.

Minor burns and scalds (superficial burns) are often caused by accidents
in the ~~home~~ house. Blisters usually form on the skin that has been damaged by
heat or friction. During healing new skin forms at the base of the blister.
This is why it is important never to break a blister.

Cool the injured skin with plenty of cold water to relieve the pain and
~~stop~~ ease the burning. Cover with a sterile dressing and bandage loosely/in to keep it
place.

Most first aid is practical common sense which you can teach yourself. It
is the assistance or treatment given to someone injured or suddenly taken
ill before the arrival of an ambulance, doctor or other qualified person.

Change the word casualty to patient throughout this document.

Health Checks Clinic

Health Checks Clinics are arranged to enable the doctors in the health centre to monitor the health of people at risk in the community. People leading busy lives do not often stop to consider their general health, and may not eat a healthy diet. Stress, smoking and drinking alcohol, coupled with a lack of real exercise can lead to serious health problems. Patients who have a family history of heart problems or have suffered from thrombosis are particularly at risk and it is essential that they have regular health checks.

The clinics are often run by the nursing staff, and a doctor will be called in if a serious problem is found. A typical health check will include

- blood pressure
- cholesterol level
- blood glucose for diabetes
- weight.

Advice on diet and exercise will be given.

Your tasks for this department are concerned with the Health Checks Clinic.

In the course of your work in this department, you may come across some medical terms which you are not familiar with. These are listed below. If there are any other words which you do not understand, look them up in a dictionary.

angina	sense of suffocation or tightness in the centre of the chest, often accompanied by pain
calcium	metallic element essential for normal development of the body – important part of bones and teeth
calorie	unit used to indicate energy value of foods
cholesterol	fat-like substance present in the blood and most tissues, especially the nervous tissue
circulation	movement (circuit) of blood around the body (cardio-vascular system)
constipation	condition when bowels are opened infrequently or incompletely (motions are dry and hard)
disease	disorder with recognisable signs and symptoms
heart attack (myocardial infarction/or coronary thrombosis)	severe chest pain resulting from the death of part of the heart muscle (myocardium) which follows the interruption of its blood supply
hormone	substance that is produced in one part of the body and is then passed into the blood stream and carried to other organs or tissues
insulin	substance that helps to control sugar levels within the body
large intestine	wide tube below the stomach where digestion of food takes place
sodium	mineral element and an important part of the body – the amount of sodium in the body is controlled by the kidneys
stroke	sudden damage to brain tissue caused by a lack of blood supply or rupture of a blood vessel; leads to weakness affecting one side of the body
thrombosis	formation of a blood clot
thyroid	organ in the neck that produces a hormone (iodine)
urination	passing of water and waste products (urea) out of the body

Health Checks Clinic Exercise 1

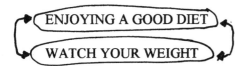
ENEnjoying A Good Diet

Watch Your Weight

copy this paragraph (C)

Healthy eating is very important for everyone, especially if you need to lower your blood cholesterol level. In order that your intake is healthy and balanced, you need to have regular meals, with daily amounts of fat, sodium, sugar and energy.

Fat is the most concentrated source of energy but it is important to limit the amount you eat as excess usually leads to weight gain.

Many different foods provide energy and this is measured in calories. To keep trim *and healthy* you need to balance the calories you eat with those you burn up during the day. You use about 100 calories for every 30 minutes spent doing housework, 200 walking briskly for 30 minutes and 300 *for* the same amount of time *when* playing tennis.

Eat more bread, potatoes, breakfast cereals, rice and pastas. These foods are only fattening if you add fat to them. Many of them have some dietary fibre which can help you to feel full and also prevent constipation.

leave at least 25mm here

Aim for at least five helpings a day of fruit, vegetables and salads. You can eat fresh, frozen or canned varieties. A glass of fruit juice, salad in a sandwich, home-made vegetable soup, two portions vegetables with a main meal and a piece of fresh fruit or fruit salad is a good example of five helpings a day.

Vitamins and minerals, sometimes called micronutrients because the body only needs them in very small amounts, are essential. Some vitamins and minerals make up much of the body's structure, tissues and fluids. Calcium is used in your teeth and bones whilst iron is found in red blood cells. Your diet will contain enough vitamins and minerals if you eat a variety of foods. Calcium is found in dairy produce and vitamin C in fruit. *and vary your intake from day to day*

(B)
the amount of
Cut down on salt and replace with herbs, spices and lemon juice to enhance the flavour of your food. Also gradually reduce the amount of sugar you add to drinks and puddings. Sweeteners can be added to drinks.

Eat at least two portions of
~~Healthy eating means eating~~ fish each week, one of which should be oily, eg salmon, mackerel, herring and trout. ~~Always use low fat cooking methods~~.

you use

Move this paragraph to (A) (B)

(A)

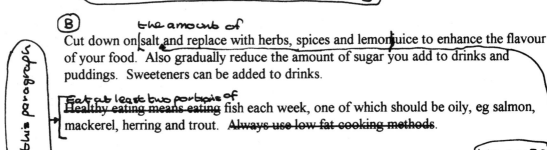
This is a draft. Make sure you save it.

Health Checks Clinic Exercise 2

THE LIBERTY HEALTH CENTRE

Health Checks Clinic ← *(Emphasise this heading)*

As part of your regular visit to our clinic your diet and weight will be discussed. Being the right weight for your height is essential for good health.

If you are overweight, we can discuss changing your eating habits. The only real way to lose weight is to exercise more.

Some healthy eating foods for breakfast include:

1 Bran flakes with banana
4 Wholemeal toast with low fat spread
3 Porridge with raisins
5 Grilled tomatoes on toast
2 Poached egg on toast
7 Low fat yoghurt with banana
6 Fruit salad and natural yoghurt

You will need to increase the amount you eat if you are under weight. Keep the foods you choose part of a healthy choice.

Enjoy your food - eating should be a pleasure.

(This is a draft. Make sure you save it)

Health Checks Clinic Exercise 3

Retain abbreviations

VITALITY AND MINERALS

Check this name from Document 1 and amend if necessary

Although all the vitamins and minerals you need can be found in your diet, various factors contribute to there being a shortage.

Please modify layout so that Minerals follows Vitamins

VITAMINS, MINERALS AND SUPPLEMENTS	RDA	SOURCE AND HEALTH CARE	
		PART OF BODY	FOOD SOURCES
Minerals			
Calcium	800mg	Bones, teeth	Milk, yoghurt
Iron	14mg	Red blood cells	Beef, spinach
Magnesium	300mg	Nervous system	Pasta, soya beans
Zinc	15mg	Enzyme production	Seafood, cereals
Iodine	150mg	Thyroid, hormones	Fishoils, kelp
Selenium	None	Defence system	Whole wheatgrain
Vitamins			
A	800mcg	Eyes, skin	Butter, liver
B1	1.4 mg	Nervous system	Brown rice, peas
C	60mg	Wound healing	Oranges, kiwi fruit
D	5mcg	Bones, teeth	Kippers, milk
E	10mg	Blood, tissues	Vegetable oils
K	None	Clotting of blood	Tomatoes, broccoli
Supplements			
Fibre	None	Large intestine	Fruit, porridge
Garlic	None	Heart	Garlic
Lec	None	Circulation	Trout, soya beans
Royal Jelly	None	General wellbeing	Worker bees
Sillicia	None	Hair, nails	Horsetail plant

If no amount is specified in the Recommended Daily Allowance column, it means it depends on individual needs.

Please sort into exact alphabetical order in the Vitamins, Minerals and Supplements column.

Please modify layout so that PART OF BODY column appears to the right of FOOD SOURCES column.

Health Checks Clinic Exercise 4

(Insert Ⓐ from following page)

Dear Mrs Mitchell

Re   Free Health Check Clinic
      Summary of what to expect

We would like to confirm your appointment at the above clinic next month. More and more people lead very busy lives and it is essential that you have a regular health check.

We will begin by taking your blood pressure. During an average day your blood pressure will vary many times, from at its lowest when you are resting to its highest at times of stress. Blood pressure is one of the most important risk factors involving heart attack, angina and strokes.

(Insert Ⓑ from following page)

We will take a blood test to determine your Cholesterol level. Cholesterol is a fatty substance used by the body to make hormones and the bile acids in the liver that help digest food. If your test is found to be high you will be given a low-fat diet to follow.

A blood glucose test will be taken for Diabetes. This is a common condition in which the amount of glucose (sugar) in the blood is too high. Depending on the result of the test, treatment can include insulin injections, diet and tablets.

Any worries you may have concerning these tests can be discussed when you keep your appointment.

Yours sincerely

Lynne Clifford
Practice Nurse

Top +2 please.
One file copy and
one for Practice Manager.
Indicate routing.

Extra Text for Exercise 4

(A) LC/your initials

Lynn Clifford
Practice Nurse

Mrs Jennifer Mitchell
49 Somerset Way
Oakhill
WELLS
BA5 3RX

(B) We will check that you are the right weight for your height and suggest a suitable diet if necessary.

Health Checks Clinic Exercise 5

Open the document you saved in Exercise 2 and make the following amendments

THE LIBERTY HEALTH CENTRE

Health Checks Clinic

As part of your regular visit to our clinic your diet and weight will be discussed. Being the right weight for your height is essential for good health.

If you are overweight, we can discuss changing your eating habits. The only real way to lose weight is to eat less and exercise more.

Some healthy eating foods for breakfast include:

1 Bran flakes with banana
4 Wholemeal toast with low-fat spread
3 Porridge with raisins
5 Grilled tomatoes on toast
2 Poached egg on toast
7 Low fat yoghurt with banana
6 Fruit salad and natural yoghurt

Sort into exact numerical order and inset 25mm from the left margin

You will need to increase the amount you eat if you are underweight. ~~Keep the foods you choose part of a healthy choice.~~ Make sure you choose only healthy food.

Enjoy your food - eating should be a pleasure. Centre this line

If you are the right weight it is important to stay that way and still eat a healthy diet.

Health Checks Clinic Exercise 6

Open the document you saved in Exercise 1 and make the following changes.

Change to double-line spacing except where indicated and use a justified right margin.

WATCH YOUR WEIGHT

Insert HEALTHY EATING as a header to appear on every page

Change the word Intake to diet throughout this document.

ENJOYING A GOOD DIET

Healthy eating is very important for everyone, especially if you need to lower your blood cholesterol level. In order that your intake is healthy and balanced, you need to have regular meals, with daily amounts of fat, sodium, sugar and ~~energy.~~ *carbohydrate.*

Fat is the most concentrated source of energy but it is important to limit the amount you eat as excess usually leads to weight gain.

Many different foods provide energy and this is measured in calories. To keep trim and healthy you need to balance the calories you eat with those you burn up during the day. You use about 100 calories for every 30 minutes spent doing housework, 200 walking briskly for 30 minutes and 300 for the same amount of time when playing tennis.

Eat more bread, potatoes, breakfast cereals, rice and pastas. These foods are only fattening if you add fat to them. Many of them have some dietary fibre which can help you to feel full and also prevent constipation.

This paragraph only in single-line spacing.

Aim for at least five helpings a day of fruit, vegetables and salads. You can eat fresh, frozen or canned varieties. A glass of fruit juice, salad in a sandwich, home-made vegetable soup, two portions *of* vegetables with a main meal and a piece of fresh fruit or fruit salad is a good example of five helpings a day.

Health Checks Clinic Exercise 6 continued

Vitamins and minerals, sometimes called micronutrients because the body only needs them in very small amounts, are essential. Some vitamins and minerals make up much of the body's structure, tissues and fluids. Calcium is used in your teeth and bones whilst iron is found in red blood cells.

Your diet will contain enough vitamins and minerals if you eat a variety of foods and vary your intake from day to day. Calcium is found in dairy produce and vitamin C ~~in~~ fruit. (is found)

Eat at least two portions of fish each week, one of which should be oily, eg salmon, mackerel, herring and trout.

Cut down on the amount of salt you use and replace ^it~ with herbs, spices and lemon juice to enhance the flavour of your food. Also gradually reduce the amount of sugar you add to drinks and puddings. Sweeteners can be added to drinks.

Healthy eating is very important for everyone, especially if you need to lower your blood cholesterol level. In order that your intake is healthy and balanced, you need to have regular meals, with daily amounts of fat, sodium, sugar and ~~energy~~ carbohydrate.

If you enjoy alcohol, drinking 1 or 2 units a day may ~~reduce~~ lower your risk of heart disease. ✓ One unit is equal to a glass of wine, and a glass of red wine may be ^particularly~ beneficial. Drinking more units a day can ~~put up~~ increase your blood pressure and damage your health.

Hospital Exercises

A District Hospital has a number of junior doctors, registrars, senior registrars, surgeons, physicians and consultants as well as nurses and auxiliary staff. They often specialise in different branches of medicine. Patients are referred to the hospital by their own doctors for specialised diagnosis or treatment. Out-patients are seen at the hospital on an appointments system, and patients who need surgery, long-term treatment or care are routinely admitted from a waiting list. Emergency cases are admitted immediately providing that a bed is available.

If you work as a medical secretary in a hospital you may be asked to complete tasks for any of the medical staff in the hospital. Some members of the medical staff carry dictation machines with them as they walk around the wards to enable them to record patient notes, and familiarity with the use of these machines would be an advantage. If you are working as a member of a team your work will include

- general correspondence relating to the care of in/out-patients
- memoranda
- reports
- circulars
- notices
- maintaining registration and appointment systems
- preparing rotas
- admissions and discharges
- follow-up systems
- waiting lists
- ward notes.

You will be working for each of the following five departments in the hospital in turn.

- Cardiology
- Orthopaedic ⎫
- Physiotherapy ⎬ Tasks from these two departments will be worked on together.
- Gynaecology
- Otorhinolaryngology

Cardiology Department

This department deals with the function of the heart, and the investigation, diagnosis and medical treatment of disorders of the heart and blood vessels. The heart is the strongest muscle in the body, and its function is to pump blood to the lungs and then to the rest of the body. The department will have at least one cardiologist (heart specialist) and nursing staff skilled in the art of healthy living by education and the care of those suffering from heart disorders. Some patients may be referred to a cardiovascular surgeon if surgical treatment is needed. Others, particularly those suffering from hypertension, may receive therapy in the form of yoga exercises. These exercises are recommended to relieve stress, one of the chief causes of hypertension. The system of yoga practised in the western world is hatha-yoga which uses a serious of poses together with special breathing techniques to relax the patient.

Your tasks in this department will be concerned with all matters involving the heart.

In the course of your work in this department, you may come across some medical terms which you are not familiar with. These are listed below. If there are any other words which you don't understand, look them up in a dictionary.

artery	blood vessel carrying blood away from the heart
cardiomyopathy	disease of the heart muscle
chest (thorax)	part of the body cavity between the neck and the diaphragm (the midriff)
conception	start of pregnancy when a male cell fertilises a female cell in the fallopian tube
hypertension	high blood pressure
membrane	thin layer of tissue surrounding part or the whole of an organ
muscle	tissue with the power to contract – enables the body to move
oxygen	odourless and colourless gas that is essential to most forms of life
plaque	flat or raised patches on the moist membrane lining tubular structures
therapy	treatment of a disease
toxic	poisonous
vein	blood vessel carrying blood towards the heart
womb (uterus)	part of the female reproductive organs; where the growing foetus (unborn child) is nourished from its mother's blood.

Cardiology Exercise 1

Copy this paragraph (A) 10

STRUCTURE, FUNCTION AND DISORDERS OF THE HEART

The heart is the strongest muscle in the body. Pear-shaped and about the size of a man's fist, it is positioned centrally in the chest. Much of the heart consists of a special type of muscle called myocardium. The interior of the heart is divided down the centre by a partition called the septum. Each half of the heart consists of an upper chamber, called an atrium and a lower chamber called a ventricle.

internal

The surface of the heart is lined with a smooth membrane called endocardium.

It's job is to pump blood through the hundreds of miles of linked arteries, veins and smaller vessels which reach out to every part of the human body. This muscular pump throughout life beats continuously and rhythmically and during an average lifetime will contract more than 2,500 million times. The heart starts beating within the womb within only a month of conception and stops only with death.

(contraction)

The heartbeat is readily felt on the left side of the chest. This beat can be located on the radial artery on the inner side of the wrist at the base of the thumb. You can also feel the beat at the cartoid artery on the side of the neck below the chin.

leave at least 50mm here

The average adult beat rate at rest is 60-80 per minute.

In developed countries, the most common cause of death is a heart disorder. Heart trouble can start in the womb. German measles during pregnancy can be one reason for this.

The most common toxic substance to affect the heart is alcohol. A large intake for many years may cause a type of cardiomyopathy in which the heart becomes enlarged. If the alcohol is stopped, recovery is possible.

Being overweight puts an extra strain on your ~~Nutritional disorders through poor diet can also cause problems for the~~ heart. Foods such as sausages, meatpies, cakes, biscuits, fried foods and dairy products increase the amount of cholesterol in your blood.

The higher the level of cholesterol, the higher the risk of heart disease.

The major cause of heart disease is impaired blood supply. The coronary arteries, which supply blood to the heart, become narrowed when fat develops on their inner walls. This causes an obstruction to the blood flow and parts of the heart muscle are deprived of oxygen.

(A)

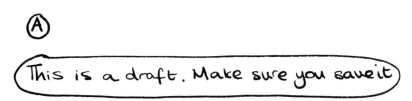

This is a draft. Make sure you save it

Cardiology Exercise 2

Quantock District Hospital

SOME CAUSES OF CORONARY HEART DISEASE

Coronary heart disease is a term used to describe the narrowing of the blood vessels that supply the heart. This narrowing is often due to a build-up of fatty plaques on the inside of the arteries.

Some of the causes of this fat build-up are:

2   hypertension
6   increased age
1   cigarette smoking
4   diabetes
3   physical inactivity
5   high blood cholesterol

Talk to your doctor about nicotine replacement therapy. This will make it easier for you to cope with nicotine withdrawal.

Choose the method that suits you best.

inhalator

Do not be tempted to substitute cigarettes by eating sweets and sugary snacks. Keep a box of celery, carrots or fresh fruit near you

Reduce your risk of heart disease – stop smoking.

Centre this line

This is a draft. Make sure you save it.

Cardiology Exercise 3

YOGA EXERCISE CLASS

Listed below are the next session of classes to be run as part of the Cardiology Department's treatment therapies. These classes will be open to patients from other surgeries in the area.

(handwritten note, left margin, vertical): Please modify layout so that Standing Movements follow Sitting Movements

INSTUCTOR'S NAME	DATE (APRIL)	DETAILS OF CLASSES	
		TIME	TYPE OF ROUTINE
Standing Movements			
DAVIES Beverley	1	0930	Breathing improvement
HOOPER Sian	8	1000	Reach-up movements
ALLEN Lindsey	15	1030	Side slides
JOHNSTON Ian	22	1500	Triangle movements
JACKSON Dolores	29	1530	Forward bends
Kneeling Movements			
ELDER Walter	1	0915	Reach-up movements
DORE Denise	8	0945	Sit down movements
FRANCIS Shona	15	1015	Back movements
GIBSON Ruta	22	1515	Uncoil movements
LEWIS Jillian	29	1545	Healthy posture
Sitting/Lying Movements			
ASHFORD Ingrid	1	0930	Head to knees
BEVAN Matthew	8	1000	Spine Twists
NOAKES Abigail	15	1030	Shoulder rotations
SHARPE Hannah	22	1500	Elbow bends
TSANG Kimba	24	1530	Corpse posture
TAYLOR Anna	29	1600	Bridge posture

These exercises help all cases of hypertension and stress.

(handwritten note, box): Please sort into exact alphabetical order by INSTRUCTOR'S NAME (SURNAME) within each section.

(handwritten note, box): Please modify layout so that TYPE OF ROUTINE column appears to the left of TIME column.

Cardiology Exercise 4

(Insert Ⓐ from next page)

Dear Dr Pierce

Re   Yoga Exercise Classes
         Details and Benefits

Thank you for enquiring about our new classes that
are due to start again in April. Any patients who are
suffering from hypertension or stress would greatly
benefit from attending these classes.

(Insert Ⓑ from next page)

As you may be aware yoga is the perfect way to exercise
as it is simply a form of relaxation and an aid to keeping
the body supple. In India its followers regard it as
a complete philosophy of life.

All our classes are taken by a qualified yoga instructor.
The classes are small in number so that patients can
be given individual attention. The instructor regularly
walks around the class observing and helping.

The treatment rooms that we use for yoga are
kept moderately warm and airy. There is space for
patients to fully stretch their body and we have
rugs for them to lie on.

Once patients have become familiar with the positions
and postures they can continue to exercise for
10-15 minutes once or twice a day in the comfort of
their own home.

Please refer any patients you may have who you feel
would benefit from this type of therapy.

Yours sincerely

Dr Jordanna Cutajar
Cardiology Clinic

(Top + 2 please.
One file copy and
one for Sian Hooper.
Indicate routing.)

Extra Text for Exercise 4

Ⓐ Our ref JC/your initials

Cardiology Clinic
Dr Jordanna Cutajar

Dr W Pierce
Somerlea Health Centre
Shepton Mallet
North Somerset
BA4 7PZ

Ⓑ Our programmes are particularly planned to relax the mind and body as well as to enhance physical well-being.

Cardiology Exercise 5

Open the document you saved in Exercise 2 and make the following changes

Quantock District Hospital ← *Emphasise this heading*

SOME CAUSES OF CORONARY HEART DISEASE

Coronary heart disease is a term used to describe the narrowing of the blood vessels that supply the heart. This narrowing is often due to a build-up of fatty plaques on the inside of the /arteries. *(walls of the)*

Some of the causes of this fat build-up are:

2 hypertension
6 increased age
1 cigarette smoking
4 diabetes
3 physical inactivity
5 high blood cholesterol

Sort into exact numerical order and inset 25mm from left margin

Talk to your doctor about nicotine replacement therapy. This will make it easier for you to cope with /nicotine withdrawal. *the physical and emotional pressures of*

Choose the method that suits you best.

gum
patch
inhalator

Do not be tempted to substitute cigarettes by eating sweets and sugary snacks. Keep a box of celery, carrots or fresh fruit near you *to use as an alternative.*

Reduce your risk of heart disease - stop smoking.

Begin a healthier lifestyle by stopping smoking cigarettes. You will soon have more energy and feel younger. It demands willpower to break the nicotine habit and it will not always be easy.

Cardiology Exercise 6

Open the document you saved in Exercise 1 and make the following amendments.

Change to double-line spacing except where indicated and use a justified right margin.

Insert THE HEART to appear as a footer on every page.

Change the word beat to pulse throughout the document.

STRUCTURE, FUNCTION AND DISORDERS OF THE HEART

The heart is the strongest muscle in the body. Pear-shaped and about the size of a man's fist, it is positioned centrally in the chest. Much of the heart consists of a special type of muscle called myocardium. The interior of the heart is divided down the centre by a partition called the septum. Each half of the heart consists of an upper chamber, called an atrium and a lower chamber called a ventricle.

The internal surface of the heart is lined with a smooth membrane called endocardium.

The heart's
~~Its~~ job is to pump blood through the hundreds of miles of linked arteries, veins and smaller vessels which reach out to every part of the human body. This muscular pump ~~throughout life~~ beats continuously and rhythmically and during an average lifetime will contract more than 2,500 million times.

The heart starts beating within the womb within only a month of conception and stops only with death.

easily
The heartbeat (contraction) is ~~readily~~ felt on the left side of the chest. This pulse can be located on the radial artery on the inner side of the wrist at the base of the thumb. You can also feel the pulse at the cartoid artery on the side of the neck below the chin. The average adult pulse rate at rest is 60-80 per minute.

In developed countries, the most common cause of death is a heart disorder. Heart trouble can start in the womb. German measles /during (or rubella) pregnancy can be one reason for this.

2

The most common toxic substance to affect the heart is alcohol. A large intake ~~for~~ *over* many years may cause a type of cardiomyopathy in which the heart becomes enlarged. If the *intake of* alcohol is stopped, recovery is possible.

Being overweight puts an extra strain on your heart. Foods such as sausages, meat pies, cakes, biscuits, fried foods and dairy products increase the amount of cholesterol in your blood.

The higher the level of cholesterol, the higher the risk of heart disease.

This paragraph only in single line spacing

The major cause of heart disease is impaired blood supply. The coronary arteries, which supply blood to the heart, become narrowed when fat develops on their inner walls. This causes an obstruction to the blood flow and parts of the heart muscle are deprived of oxygen.

The heart is the strongest muscle in the body. Pear-shaped and about the size of a man's fist, it is positioned centrally in the chest. Much of the heart consists of a special type of muscle called myocardium. The interior of the heart is divided down the centre by a partition called the septum. Each half of the heart consists of an upper chamber, called an atrium, and a lower chamber, called a ventricle.

Move this paragraph A on previous page. P

It is now widely known that smoking by an expectant mother can have a serious effect on the heart. It has a toxic effect on her circulatory system and usually results in a smaller, potentially ~~less strong weaker~~ baby. In adult years, smoking is known to have a damaging effect on arteries. ✓

Orthopaedic and Physiotherapy Departments

Disorders of the bones and joints and the muscles, tendons and ligaments associated with them are diagnosed and treated in the Orthopaedic Department. There will be at least one orthopaedic surgeon in the department and he or she will be supported by other doctors and nurses. Some disorders or deformities may require surgery, and these will include setting of broken bones and repairing or replacing hip, knee or finger joints. Other treatments may include traction and manipulation. Slipped discs, arthritis, dislocations and birth defects of the skeleton may also be treated within the department.

Following treatment in the Orthopaedic Department, patients will often be referred to the Physiotherapy Department for physical treatment. This treatment is used to reduce joint stiffness and to restore muscle strength. It is also used to retrain joints and muscles after stroke or nerve injury, to reduce inflammation, pain and muscle spasm. There are three kinds of treatment as follows.

- Physical – exercises, both passive and active, therapeutic massage and manipulation.
- Heat – ultrasound, short wave, TENS, cold and hydrotherapy.
- Respiratory – breathing exercises, percussion and postural drainage.

There will usually be a small team of physiotherapists operating in the department, and they will also go into the wards to check on the respiratory condition of patients who are on ventilators or are recovering from major surgery.

Your tasks in these departments are concerned with the diagnosis and treatment of patients with skeletal or breathing disorders.

In the course of your work in these departments, you may come across some medical terms which you are not familiar with. These are listed below. If there are any other words which you do not understand, look them up in a dictionary.

anti-inflammatory	drug that reduces inflammation
bone marrow	soft substance inside bones
bronchitis	inflammation of the bronchi (tubes connecting the windpipe to the lungs; also the smaller tubes within the lungs)
cartilage	hard, but flexible, substance which forms part of the skeleton
diathermy	production of heat in a part of the body by means of high-frequency electric current passed from electrodes placed on the skin
disc	rounded flattened structure such as an intervertebral disc (back bone)
hydrotherapy	treatment using water, eg baths
ligaments	tough band of fibrous tissue that links two bones together at a joint (joint capsule)
manipulation	use of the hands to produce movement of bones, joints or soft tissues as part of treatment
massage	manipulation of the soft tissue of the body
menopause	the end of reproductive life in women when menstruation finally stops
metabolism	the sum of all the chemical and physical changes that take place within the body and enable its continued growth and functioning
osteoporosis	abnormality in which bones become dense and brittle and tend to fracture; common in the elderly

platelets	small disc-shaped bodies in the blood which play an important role in coagulation
percussion	diagnostic technique for examining the chest or abdomen by tapping it with the fingers and listening to the resonance of the sound produced
postural drainage	technique that enables a person whose lungs are clogged with sputum to drain them
respiratory system	the organs and tissues that enable air to pass in and out of the body (lungs), ie breathing
sputum (phlegm)	mucous material released from glands in the walls of the main airways in the lungs
tendon	tough cord that attaches the end of a muscle to a bone
TENS	transcutaneous electrical nerve stimulation – pain relief by the application of tiny electrical impulses to nerve endings under the skin
ultrasound	ultrasonic waves – sound waves of extremely high frequency that cannot be heard by the human ear

2

Orthopaedic/Physiotherapy Exercise 1

Insert Osteoarthritis to appear as a header on every page

This is a draft. Make sure you save it.

BONE AND JOINT DISORDERS

THE HUMAN SKELETON

The structure of a bone

~~Bone structure~~ consists of several layers. A thin membranous surface contains a network of blood vessels and nerves. Beneath is a hard, dense shell that is known as compact, ivory or cortical bone. Inside this shell is a spongy material in which the bone marrow lies. Red cells, called platelets and most white blood cells are formed in the bone marrow.

Orthopaedic surgeons are concerned with disorders of the bones and joints, together with their associated muscles, tendons and ligaments. They set broken bones, treat joint conditions such as dislocations, slipped discs, arthritis and back problems. Surgical repair or replacement hips, knees or finger joints are also part of their work. ~~Research is always being done to improve replacement joints.~~ [A joint is a junction between two or more bones. Some joints are fixed, others are mobile, or allow only a small amount of movement. Common joint wounds include sprains, damage to the cartilage, torn ligaments and tearing of the joint capsule.

Joints are commonly affected by forms of arthritis (inflammation of a joint). Bursitis (inflammation of a bursa — a small sac of fibrous tissue that is lined with membrane and filled with fluid), ¶ Bursae occur where parts move over one another; they help to reduce friction.

may occur as a result of a strain.

Permanent joint deformities may be caused by severe wounds. Surgery may be required to correct certain deformities.

or part of a joint

Some joints can be replaced by metal or plastic components. Hip replacements have been taking place since the 1930s. ~~During the 1960s this work was really revolutionised.~~ Knee joint replacement is now as successful as hip joint replacement. Finger, shoulder and elbow joints are now also replacements. Engineers and orthopaedic surgeons are still developing and improving replacement joints of all kinds.

It can also affect old wounds years later.

copy this paragraph ⑩ to

Osteoarthritis is a degenerative joint disease resulting from wear and tear. It affects mainly the hip, knee, spine and fingers. Women, particularly during the menopause, are more likely to be affected than men.

Leave at least 25mm here

The   of osteoarthritis

~~Osteoarthritis~~ symptoms are a swelling and deformity in one or more joints with a slow onset of pain. If the fingers are affected the joints become lumpy. Osteoarthritis is progressive and irreversible. Only a few sufferers become severely disabled. Most are able to lead ordinary lives but some ~~activities~~ *functions* may need to be modified to preserve joint functions. Diseased joints that have become unstable and extremely painful may require arthroplasty.

Ⓑ

Orthopaedic/Physiotherapy Exercise 2

QUANTOCK DISTRICT HOSPITAL

Food Fact Sheet ◄───────── *Emphasise this heading*

To follow a healthy course between processed foods towards naturally nutritious foods, you need to know some basic facts about proteins, fats and carbohydrates. You must get these in the most natural form possible. Listed below are a few recipe ideas you may not have tried before.

2 Fruit nog
6 Chinese celery soup
1 Vichyssoise
4 Tomato surprise
3 Pears with raspberry sauce
5 Soybean soup

Protein is the main structural component of tissue and organs, and it is needed for growth and repair of cells. It is found mainly in eggs, cheese and milk.

Fats also provide energy but care should be taken that they do not constitute more than 30 percent of total calorie intake.

This is a draft. Make sure you save it

Orthopaedic/Physiotherapy Exercise 3

QUANTOCK DISTRICT HOSPITAL

The following appointments have been made for the Physiotherapy Department today.

PATIENT'S NAME	APPOINTMENT TIME	GENERAL DETAILS	
		TREATMENT	DISORDER/INJURY

Appointments for Yvonne Minter, Senior Physiotherapist

ATKINSON Kay	0900	Passive exercise	Nerve injury
CHAPMAN Angela	0930	Therapeutic massage	Back pain
BISHOP Karen	1000	Ice packs	Swelling on arm
EASTON John	1400	Active exercise	Stroke
DICKINSON Allan	1430	Ultrasound	Knee ligament

Appointments for Shauna Wood, Physiotherapist

BLACKLOCK Jeremy	1000	Diathermy	Rheumatism
GRECH Susan	1030	TENS	Arthritis
CHIVERS Paul	1100	Passive exercise	Nerve injury
LOCKART Edwin	1130	Manipulation	Frozen shoulder
MORTON Helen	1200	Ultrasound	Tennis elbow
NAKAMURA Milan	1230	Therapeutic massage	Back pain

Appointments for Lesley Donnolly, Physiotherapist

ADAMS Deidre	1430	Active exercise	Stroke
BAILEY Neil	1500	Ultrasound	Ankle joint
COLE James	1530	Diathermy	Rheumatism
DIXON Mavis	1600	Hydrotherapy	Osteoarthritis
GRIFFITHS Irene	1600	Hydrotherapy	Osteoarthritis

Yvonne Minter will be visiting the wards from 1030 to 12 noon to check on respiratory diseases, eg chronic bronchitis, giving breathing exercises etc.

Please modify layout so that Shauna Wood's appointments follow Lesley Donnolly's appointments.

Please sort into exact alphabetical order by PATIENT SURNAME within each section.

Please modify layout so that DISORDER/INJURY column appears to the left of TREATMENT column.

Orthopaedic/Physiotherapy Exercise 4

(Insert Ⓐ on following page)

Dear Dr Broadstone

Re   Mrs Jacky Walters   DoB 18/10/40
     18 Cherry Blossom Way   WELLS   BA5 4QT

This lady has now completed a course of treatment here
for osteoarthritis in her knees. She also has the disease
in her spine but this is not causing her too much pain at
the moment. She has been a typist all her working life
and the possibility of a poorly designed chair could be
part of her back problem.

Degeneration of the cartilage that lines the hinge joint
of the knees has caused her to have pain and stiffness.
There are also signs of osteophytes at the margins of the
joint surfaces. These bony outgrowths are another
reason for her discomfort.

(Insert Ⓑ on following page)

She is taking Ibuprofen tablets, 400 mg three times
a day with no side effects. Although she is in
remission from pain at the moment, I would suggest
she continues with this dosage. If a flare-up occurs,
corticosteroid injections could be used.

Would you please refer her again in 6 months time for
another series of exercises in our hydrotherapy pool.

Yours sincerely

Yvonne Minter MCSP
Senior Physiotherapist

Top + 2 please.
One file copy and
one for Robert Parsons,
Hydrotherapy Pool
Manager.
Indicate routing.

Extra Text for Exercise 4

(A)

Physiotherapy Department
Senior Physiotherapist
Yvonne Minter MCSP

Our ref YM/your initials/PH700976194
Dr W Broadstone
The Liberty Health Centre
The Liberty
WELLS
BAS 2FX

(B) She has had swimming exercises in our hydrotherapy pool. The buoyant effect of the water has allowed fuller use of her joints with little discomfort. These swimming exercises have also been beneficial for her back.

Orthopaedic/Physiotherapy Exercise 5

Open the document you saved in Exercise 2 and make the following changes.

QUANTOCK DISTRICT HOSPITAL

Food Fact Sheet for Arthritis sufferers

To follow a healthy course from processed foods towards naturally nutritious foods, you need to know some basic facts about proteins, fats and carbohydrates. You must get these in the most natural form possible. Listed below are a few recipe ideas you may not have tried before.

2 Fruit nog
6 Chinese celery soup
1 Vichyssoise
4 Tomato surprise
3 Pears with raspberry sauce
5 Soybean soup

Sort into exact numerical order and inset 25 mm from the left margin.

Protein is the main structural component of tissue and organs, and it is needed for growth and repair of cells. It is found mainly in eggs, cheese and milk.

Centre this paragraph

Fats also provide energy but care should be taken that they do not contain constitute more than 30 per cent of the total calorie intake.

A vegan diet, which excludes dairy produce, needs careful planning to prevent protein deficiency.

Sugars and starches are the two carbohydrates food groups. They are the main energy sources required for metabolism and they should take make up at least half of the diet.

Orthopaedic/Physiotherapy Exercise 6

OSTEOARTHRITIS

Open the document you saved in Exercise 1 and make the following changes.

THE HUMAN SKELETON

Change to double-line spacing unless otherwise indicated and use a justified right margin

BONE AND JOINT DISORDERS

Move this paragraph to (A)

The structure of a bone consists of several layers. A thin membranous surface contains a network of blood vessels and nerves. Beneath is a hard, dense shell that is known as compact, ivory or cortical bone. Inside this shell is a spongy material in which the bone marrow lies. Red cells, called platelets and most white blood cells are formed in the bone marrow.

Orthopaedic surgeons are concerned with disorders of the bones and joints, together with their associated muscles, tendons and ligaments. They set broken bones, treat joint conditions such as dislocations, slipped discs, arthritis and back problems. Surgical repair or replacement hips, knees or finger joints are also part of their work.

Change the word wounds to injuries throughout the document.

A joint is a junction between two or more bones. Some joints are ~~fixed~~ *mobile*, others are ~~mobile~~ *fixed*, or allow only a small amount of movement. Common joint wounds include sprains, damage to the cartilage, torn ligaments and tearing of the joint capsule.

Joints are commonly affected by forms of arthritis (inflammation of a joint). Bursitis (inflammation of a bursa - a small sac of fibrous tissue that is lined with membrane and filled with fluid), may occur as a result of a strain. Bursae occur where parts move over one another; they help to reduce friction.

Permanent joint deformities may be caused by severe wounds. *or arthritis* Surgery may be required to correct certain deformities.

This paragraph only in single-line spacing

Some joints (or part *is* of a joint) can be replaced by metal or plastic components. Hip replacements have been taking place since the 1930s. Knee joint replacement is now as successful as hip joint replacement. Finger joint, shoulder and elbow joints are now also replace*d* ~~ments~~. Engineers and orthopaedic surgeons are still developing and improving replacement joints of all kinds.

This is called arthroplasty.

Orthopaedic/Physiotherapy Exercise 6 continued

OSTEOARTHRITIS

Osteoarthritis is a degenerative joint disease resulting from wear and tear.
It can also affect old wounds years later. It affects mainly the hip, knee,
spine and fingers. Women, ~~particularly~~ especially during the menopause, are more
likely to be affected than men.

The symptoms of osteoarthritis are a swelling and deformity in one or
more joints with a slow onset of pain. If the fingers are affected the joints
become lumpy. Osteoarthritis is progressive and irreversible. Only a few
sufferers become severely disabled. Most are able to lead ~~ordinary~~ normal lives
but some activities may need to be modified to preserve joint functions.
Diseased joints that have become unstable and extremely painful may
require arthroplasty.

Osteoarthritis is a degenerative joint disease resulting from wear and tear.
It can also affect old wounds years later. It affects mainly the hip, knee,
spine and fingers. Women, ~~particularly~~ especially during the menopause, are more
likely to be affected than men.

Anti-inflammatory drugs are used for the treatment
of osteoarthritis, and physiotherapy may be
arranged to strengthen weak muscles. A few days'
bed rest will help to settle inflammation. People
who are overweight should try to lose weight
as placing abnormal weight on the knees or
hips may cause the disease to develop.

Gynaecology Department

The female reproductive system is dealt with in the Gynaecology Department. The work of the department includes the investigation and treatment of menstrual problems, menopausal problems and other problems affecting the female reproductive tract. These include

- fibroids
- ovarian cysts
- cervical polyps.

Advice may be given about methods of contraception. Surgery in the department includes dilatation and curettage (D and C) and hysterectomy. Drug therapy is used to treat some conditions. Disorders in early pregnancy such as recurrent miscarriage are also part of this department's work, although pregnancy is handled by the Obstetrics Department. There will be at least one gynaecologist in the department, who will also be a specialist in obstetrics, and nursing staff to oversee the care of patients within the department.

Your tasks in this department are concerned with the diagnosis and treatment of patients with disorders of the female reproductive system.

In the course of your work in this department, you may come across some medical terms which you are not familiar with. These are listed below. If there are any other words which you do not understand, look them up in a dictionary.

Bartholin's glands	pair of glands that open at the junction of the vagina and the vulva
bladder	organ that stores urine produced by the kidneys
cervical cancer	cancer of the neck (cervix) of the uterus
clitoris	small sensitive organ in women; part of the reproductive organs
D and C (dilatation and curettage)	procedure in which the lining of the uterus is scraped away
dysplasia	abnormal development of skin, bone and other tissue
endometrium	mucous membrane lining the inside of the uterus
fallopian tubes	two tubes that carry the ova from the ovaries to the uterus
follicle	very small sac or gland in the ovary in which the ova are formed
hysterectomy	surgical operation to remove the uterus
incontinence	involuntary urination
insomnia	difficulty in getting to sleep or staying asleep
menstruation	discharge of blood from the vagina on a monthly cycle
ovaries	glands which produce ova (egg cells) in women
rectum	last part of the large intestine
uterus	part of the female reproductive tract where the fetus (unborn child) grows
vagina	muscular passage leading to the uterus
vulva	the female external genitalia (reproductive organs) – two pairs of fleshy folds surrounding the opening of the vagina

Gynaecology Exercise 1

(REPRODUCTIVE ORGANS)

(THE FEMALE GENITAL SYSTEM)

(A)

The parts of the female body concerned with reproduction include the ovaries, fallopian tubes, uterus, vagina, vulva, ~~breasts and nipples.~~ *clitoris and Bartholin's glands.* With the exception of the vulva, these reproductive organs lie within the pelvic cavity.

About two months before a baby girl is born her ovaries contain 7 million cells, this number dropping to about 1 million at birth. At puberty about 300,000 cells remain, each of which could develop into a follicle, which produces hormones and an egg. For many females the period between the start of menstruation and the menopause is about 30-40 years. Normally only one egg is produced each month, meaning that ~~about only~~ *approximately* 400 cells actually turn into eggs.

The normal functioning of the female reproductive system begins at puberty with the onset of menstruation and the potential for reproduction ends at the time of the menopause.

(copy this paragraph to (A))

Menstruation identifies the fertile years of a ~~woman's~~ *female's* life. Menstrual periods will usually begin between the ages of 11 to 16 years. At the beginning of the menstrual cycle, oestrogen hormones cause the mucous membrane lining the uterus to thicken, preparing for the possibility of fertilization. This is known as the follicular phase ~~or proliferative phase.~~ *(✓)*

Egg release (ovulation) usually occurs in the middle of the menstrual cycle. Ova are released from the ovaries. Adjacent to each ovary is a fallopian tube, which carries ova to the uterus. The uterus is a hollow pear-shaped organ situated between the bladder and the rectum. [Also at the middle of the menstrual cycle the hormone progesterone *together with oestrogen* increases production causing the endometrium to become richly supplied with blood in preparation for pregnancy.

Blood loss varies from female to female and from cycle to cycle, the average being 60 ml. The menstrual cycle is counted from the first day of loss of blood to the last day before the next menstrual bleeding.

In 95 percent of females this average number of days is 28. The average length of periods is 5 days.

Abnormal menstruation is one of the most common disorders which affects females of all ages. The most common of these disorders is painful periods (Dysmenorrhoea) and [the cause is unknown] in the majority of females. ~~Irregularity and heavy periods are other common disorders.~~

but can vary from between one day to 8 days

leave at least 50mm here

This is a draft. Make sure you save it

Gynaecology Exercise 2

QUANTOCK DISTRICT HOSPITAL

Well Woman Clinics:-   ← (Emphasise this heading)

All women between the ages of 40-60 years are being referred by their doctors to attend the above clinics.

A quarter of all women going through the menopause have symptoms that are upsetting enough to need medical help. Some of these symptoms include

abnormal periods
fatigue
hot flushes
headaches
insomnia
night sweats
hair and skin changes
vaginal dryness
depression

The drug HRT (Hormone Replacement Therapy) can be prescribed if a hysterectomy has not been performed. This treatment involves having low doses of the hormones oestrogen and progesterone. It can be prescribed in tablet form, as implant pellets under the skin or as skin patches.

It has been shown to prevent osteoporosis.

(centre this sentence)

(This is a draft. Make sure you save it)

Gynaecology Exercise 3

QUANTOCK AREA HOSPITAL

(Check the name of the Hospital from Exercise 2 and amend if necessary)

Listed below are the patients who have been referred from local Health Centres to be seen at the next Well Woman Clinic.

The Liberty Health Centre

PATIENT'S NAME	PATIENT NUMBER		AGE	REFERRAL DETAILS SYMPTOMS
FRANKLIN	Peta	117	54	Night sweats, hot flushes
BAILEY	Stacey	168	49	Vaginal dryness
O'BRIEN	Bernadette	172	44	Abnormal periods
MILLER	Audrey	193	51	Stress incontinence
STOCK	Sandra	196	47	Depression, headaches

The Crossways Health Centre

BARRETT	Barbara	47	55	Loss of self-confidence
TURNER	Joyce	101	40	Night sweats, hot flushes
YOUNG	Edna	116	51	Insomnia, Night sweats
WILLIAMS	Rose	149	56	Vaginal dryness
GRUBELIC	Carol	182	44	Headaches, anxiety

The Mendip View Health Centre

SQUIRES	Jean	65	47	Abnormal periods
JACKSON	Eileen	49	60	Night sweats, hot flushes
SINGH	Jenny	131	57	Stress incontinence
POTTER	Victoria	128	40	Vaginal dryness
ARMSTRONG	Freda	178	53	Insomnia, depression
WHITBY	Phyllis	162	56	Loss of self-confidence

Appointment letters need to be sent out one month in advance.

Move this line so that it comes before PATIENT'S NAME

Please sort into exact PATIENT NUMBER order. Ensure that all corresponding details are also re-arranged

Please move AGE column to come after SYMPTOMS column

Gynaecology Exercise 4

(Insert Ⓐ from following page)

Dear Dr Wright
Re Mrs Pauline Robinson DOB 13/3/44
   14 Cheddar View WELLS BAS 3RP

This lady was seen today at our Well Woman Clinic.
She has suffered from insomnia and depression since
the onset of her menopause at the age of 47. In the course
of our discussions together it appears that her main worry is
fear of cervical cancer. I have made an ~~appointment~~ appointment for her
to attend one of our informal therapy treatment clinics. This
involves a very practical approach to problem solving on an
individual basis. If her depression persists, I would suggest
a course of treatment on the antidepressant drug Diazepam.

She has never had a cervical smear test to detect abnormal
changes in the cells of the cervix. I explained to her that the
test has a 95% chance of detecting dysplasia. If these
abnormal cells are not discovered and treated, they can
become cancerous.

She has agreed to see you again and to have a smear
taken. Her monthly bleeding ceased two years ago and she
has not had any vaginal bleeding or bloodstained discharge
since.

(Insert Ⓑ from following page)

Yours sincerely

Dr Nicola Heritage

(Top + 2 please.
One file copy and one
for Dr Edward Hutton
Senior Gynaecologist
    Indicate
      routing)

Extra Text for Exercise 4

Ⓐ

well woman Clinic
Dr Nicola Heritage

Our ref NH/your initials/194
Dr A J Wright
The Liberty Health Centre
The Liberty
WELLS
BAS 2FX

Ⓑ *Should the result of her smear be positive, would you please refer her to Dr Edward Hutton, Senior Gynaecologist at this hospital.*

Gynaecology Exercise 5

Open the document you saved in Exercise 2 and make the following changes.

QUANTOCK DISTRICT HOSPITAL

Well Woman Clinics:- *The Menopause*

and

All women between the ages of 40/60 years are being referred by their doctors to ~~attend~~ the above clinics.

A quarter of all women going through the menopause have symptoms that are upsetting enough to ~~need~~ *require* medical help. Some of these symptoms include :

abnormal periods
fatigue
hot flushes
headaches
insomnia
night sweats
hair and skin changes
vaginal dryness
depression

Sort into exact alphabetical order and inset 25 mm from the margin

The drug HRT (Hormone Replacement Therapy) can be prescribed if a hysterectomy has not been performed. This treatment involves ~~having~~ low doses of the hormones oestrogen and progesterone. It can be prescribed in tablet form, as implant pellets under the skin or as skin patches.

✓

It has been shown to prevent/ *the development of* osteoporosis.

Centre this sentence

The menopause is the time of life when physical and psychological changes occur as a result of reduced production of the oestrogen hormones. This female hormone has a protective effect on the heart and bones. The number of heart attacks and strokes in women rises dramatically after the menopause.

Gynaecology Exercise 6

Open the document you saved in Exercise 1 and make the following changes

Change to double-line spacing except where indicated and use a justified right margin.

Change periods to bleeding throughout the document.

Insert a header: MONTHLY CYCLE to appear on every page.

THE FEMALE GENITAL SYSTEM

REPRODUCTIVE ORGANS

The normal functioning of the female reproductive system begins at puberty with the onset of menstruation and the potential for reproduction ends at the time of the menopause.

The parts of the female body concerned with reproduction include the ovaries, fallopian tubes, uterus, vagina, clitoris, vulva, and Bartholin's glands. With the exception of the vulva, these reproductive organs lie within the pelvic cavity.

About ~~two~~ **2** months before a baby girl is born her ovaries contain 7 million cells, this number dropping to about 1 million at birth. At puberty about 300,000 cells remain, each of which could develop into a follicle, which produces hormones and an egg. For many females the period between the start of menstruation and the menopause is about 30-40 years. Normally only one egg is produced each month, meaning that approximately 400 cells actually turn into eggs. *the rest degenerate.*

The normal functioning of the female reproductive system begins at puberty with the onset of menstruation and the potential for reproduction ends at the time of the menopause.

Menstruation identifies the fertile years of a female's life. Menstrual periods will usually begin between the ages of 11 ~~to~~ **and** 16 years. At the beginning of the menstrual cycle, oestrogen hormones cause the mucous membrane lining the uterus to thicken, preparing for the possibility of fertilisation. This is known as the follicular phase.

Egg release (ovulation) usually occurs in the middle of the menstrual cycle. Ova are released from the ovaries. Adjacent to each ovary is a fallopian tube, which carries ova to the uterus. The uterus is a hollow pear-shaped organ situated between the bladder and the rectum.

In
~~Also at~~ the middle of the menstrual cycle the hormone progesterone
~~together with~~ and oestrogen increases production causing the endometrium to
become richly supplied with blood in preparation for pregnancy.

this paragraph only should be fine spacing

Blood loss varies from female to female and from cycle to cycle, the
average being 60 ml. The menstrual cycle is counted from the first day of
loss of blood to the last day before the next menstrual bleeding. In 95 per
cent of females the average number of days is 28. The average length of
periods is 5 days but can vary ~~from~~ between ~~one day to~~ and 8 days.

Abnormal menstruation is one of the most common disorders which
affects females of all ages. The most common of these disorders is painful
periods (Dysmenorrhoea) and in the majority of females the cause is
unknown.

If pregnancy fails to occur, the cycle continues with the production of oestrogen and progesterone from the ovaries diminishing. The retaining fluid in the endometrium is not required and is shed about 14 days after the start of ovulation.

Otorhinolaryngology Department

2

This department is probably better known as ear, nose and throat (ENT). It deals with problems in the middle ear, sinuses and larynx, including

- minor hearing loss
- Meniere's disease
- tonsillitis
- uncontrollable nosebleeds
- airway problems in children
- cancer of the larynx and sinuses.

Tonsillitis is treated by bed rest and an analgesic or in some cases an antibiotic drug. Frequent attacks of severe tonsillitis may necessitate a tonsillectomy. Meniere's disease is treated by bed rest and antihistamine drugs, and relief from nausea and tinnitus may be obtained by taking antiemetic drugs. Antibiotic drugs are often prescribed for patients with inflammation of the sinuses together with decongestant drugs. Severe cases may require surgical drainage of the affected sinuses.

The department will have at least one ENT specialist on the staff, supported by other doctors and nurses.

Your tasks in this department are concerned with the diagnosis and treatment of ear, nose and throat conditions.

In the course of your work in this department, you may come across some medical terms which you are not familiar with. These are listed below. If there are any other words which you do not understand, look them up in a dictionary.

adenoidectomy	surgical operation to remove the adenoids
adenoids	overgrowth of glandular tissue at the rear of the nose
amalgam	filling made by mixing a silver-tin alloy with mercury in a machine known as an amalgamator
biopsy	removal of a small piece of living tissue from an organ for microscopic examination
cavity	hollow enclosed area; in dentistry, a hole in a tooth
eardrum (tympanic)	the membrane at the inner end of the external tube, separating the outer and middle ears
eustachian tube	connects the middle ear to the pharynx
gingivitis	inflammation of the gums
halitosis	bad breath
labyrinth	system of cavities and ducts involved in hearing and balance
larynx	organ of the voice; also an air passage from the pharynx to the lungs
malignant	describing any disorder or tumour that becomes life-threatening if untreated
mastoidectomy	surgical operation to remove some or all of the cells in the bone behind the ear when they have become infected
myringotomy	cut or incision of the eardrum to make an artificial opening
oesophagus	the gullet – a muscular tube that extends from the pharynx to the stomach
pharynx	throat

polyp	growth, usually benign (not malignant) attached to the surface from which it is growing by a stalk, commonly found in the nose and sinuses
respiratory system	the organs and tissues that enable air to pass in and out of the body (breathing)
radiotherapy	(treatment by) x-rays, beta rays or gamma rays
tinnitus	any ringing or buzzing noise in the ear
tonsils	two glands on either side of the back of the mouth – help protect the body from infection
tract	organ or collection of organs, enabling the passage of something
vertigo	spinning sensation, there may be a feeling that the ground is tilting – feeling of constant movement

Otorhinolaryngology Exercise 1

(Retain abbreviations)

EAR, NOSE AND THROAT SURGERY

OTORHINOLARYNGOLOGY

and

(copy this paragraph to A)

ENT Specialists commonly treat otitis media (middle ear infection) Meniere's disease (disease of the middle ear that causes progressive deafness). Otitis externa is an infection of the outer ear canal and can occur at any age, especially among swimmers.

Otits media is inflammation of the middle ear - the cavity between the eardrum and the inner ear. There are three variations of this inflammation: acute, chronic-secretory and chronic-suppurative.

Acute otitis media affects babies and very young children and the symptoms are sudden ear ache, tinnitus (ringing or buzzing in the ear) and a fever.

Chronic-suppurative otitis media is a persistent infection of the middle ear affecting older children and adults. ~~It can be treated by myringotomy.~~

Ⓐ

Meniere's disease is a condition in which the body's balance mechanism in the inner ear becomes swollen. In 85 per cent of cases only one ear is affected. The main symptom is a sudden attack of vertigo with a sensation of the room spinning round. The disease is caused by an increase in the amount of fluid in the membranous labyrinth.

(Leave at least 50mm here)

The nose is the uppermost part of the respiratory tract and it is the organ of smell. Sinus, a cavity within a bone, lined with mucous membrane surrounds the nose. Mucus produced by this membrane drains into the nasal cavity via narrow channels. Surgical drainage of affected sinuses is a common operation in this department.

(Move this paragraph to B)

Malignant tumours of the throat may be removed by surgery or treated with radiotherapy. Anti-cancer drugs may also be given. These ~~tumours~~ growths need early medical attention. ~~Difficulty in swallowing solid food is one of the symptoms.~~ They can occur in men or women and are most common in smokers.

both

The highest incidence of pharyngeal cancer is in those who smoke and drink alcohol.

The throat is the passage running down from the back of the mouth and nose to the upper part of the oesophagus and the opening into the larynx. Tonsillectomy is the name for the surgical removal of the tonsils. A tube is placed down the patient's wind pipe, or trachea, to allow during the operation him or her to breathe. The tongue is ~~clamped down~~ depressed and the tonsils are prised from the back of the throat and cut away.

Ⓑ

(With the patient under a general anaesthetic)

(This is a draft. Make sure you save it.)

Otorhinolaryngology Exercise 2

QUANTOCK DISTRICT HOSPITAL

Oral Hygiene Notes

Good oral hygiene reduces the incidence of tooth decay, it prevents gingivitis and other gum disorders and helps to prevent halitosis.

Teeth should be brushed at least once a day to remove plaque. This is an almost invisible film of bacteria that forms on the surface of the teeth particularly between the teeth and just below the gum line.

A useful glossary of dentistry would include the following:

1 anaesthetics
4
3
5
2 bridges
7
6 implanting

Bad decay is the usual reason for tooth extraction. Difficult extractions needing a general anaesthetic are ~~executed~~ executed in hospital.

(Centre this section)

(This is a draft. Make sure you save it)

Otorhinolaryngology Exercise 3

QUANTOCK DISTRICT HOSPITAL

Listed below are the operations that have taken place including ENT patients over the last 3 months.

NAME OF PATIENT	MONTH OF OPERATION	NAME OF OPERATION	CHILD/ADULT

Check the name of this operation and amend from Exercise 1 if necessary.

Surgeon - Mr Yowles - Theatre Number 4

Jade ATKINS	January	Tonsillectomy	Child
Gemma BOURNE	March	Tonsillectomy	Child
Wayne COOK	January	Sinus drainage	Child
Kim CARBONARA	February	Nasal polyp	Child
Ben HUGHES	March	Tonsillectomy	Child

Surgeon - Mr Ryan - Theatre Number 5

Erica DEMAJO	February	Myringotomy	Adult
Kimberley GRAY	January	Mastoidectomy	Adult
Ann CROSS	February	Nasal polyp	Adult
Andrew GRIFFITHS	March	Tonsillectomy	Adult
David PENN	March	Pharyngeal Cancer biopsy	Adult
Mandy REID	January	Pharyngeal Cancer biopsy	Adult

Please move ADULT/CHILD column to come before NAME OF OPERATION column.

Surgeon - Mr Reeve - Theatre Number 3

Patricia ANSWAN	March	Adenoidectomy	Child
Michelle HURST	February	Tonsillectomy	Child
George DALE	March	Mastoidectomy	Child
Keith WATSON	January	Tonsillectomy	Child
Edith WILSON	January	Adenoidectomy	Child

The number of Tonsillitus operations has increased during this period.

Please move Theatre 3 details to above Theatre 4

Please sort into alphabetical order of patients' surnames

Otorhinolaryngology Exercise 4

(Insert Ⓐ from following page)

Dear Dr Dixon

Re Mr William John Cates   DOB 19/12/70
    44 Timber Way GLASTONBURY BA5 9QL

Thank you for your letter about the above-named patient who returned to work as a cleaner at the beginning of last month. I note that he soon developed rhinorrhoea and sneezing attacks. I understand there is a family history of hay fever and migraine.

On examination, his upper respiratory tract looked clean and healthy. An x-ray showed that his sinuses were clear, although there was some sign of inflammation of his nasal septum to the right which tends to be the worst nostril.

(Insert Ⓑ from following page)

I have suggested he continues with his Beconase Aqueous nasal spray giving a metered spray of 50 micrograms of Beclomethasone dipropionate. This corticosteroid drug does not have any serious side effects for him.

If his problems persist, I should be glad to see him again.

Yours sincerely

Henry MacDonald
Consultant Surgeon

Top +2 please
One file copy and
one for X-ray Department.
Indicate routing

Extra Text for Exercise 4

Ⓐ

Otorhinolaryngology Clinic
Consultant Surgeon
Dr Henry Mac Donald

HMD / your initials / ENT 94005
Dr A Dixon
The Liberty Health Centre
The Liberty
WELLS
BA5 2FX

Ⓑ As his symptoms appear all year round, he shows no sign of recovering from his allergy to dust or house-dust mites. I have reminded him to damp dust if possible, and vacuum clean furniture and carpets frequently to keep dust levels down. He may ~~teave~~ have to consider a change of employment.

Otorhinolaryngology Exercise 5

Open the document you saved in Exercise 2 and make the following changes.

QUANTOCK DISTRICT HOSPITAL

Oral Hygiene Notes ← Emphasise this heading

occurrence
Good oral hygiene reduces the ~~incidence~~ of tooth decay, it prevents gingivitis and other gum disorders and/helps to prevent halitosis. (also)

Plaque
Teeth should be brushed at least once a day to remove plaque. ~~This~~ is an almost invisible film of bacteria that forms on the surface of the teeth particularly between the teeth and just below the gum line. ◄

A useful glossary of dentistry would include the following:

1 anaesthetics
4 fillings
3 crowns
5 amalgam
2 bridges
7 x-rays
6 implanting

Sort this into exact numerical order and inset 25mm from the left margin

which require
Bad decay is the usual reason for tooth extraction. Difficult extractions ~~needing~~ a general anaesthetic are executed in hospital.

Running dental floss through your teeth once a day removes food particles and helps to prevent plaque from building up. After flossing, rinse the mouth, drawing water through the teeth.

Use a fluoride toothpaste as products containing fluoride have been shown to reduce decay by about 25 per cent when used regularly.

Otorhinolaryngology Exercise 6

Open the document you saved in Exercise 1 and make the following changes.

Change to double-line spacing except where indicated and use a justified right margin

Insert ENT to appear as a footer on every page

OTORHINOLARYNGOLOGY

EAR, NOSE AND THROAT SURGERY

lower case

ENT Specialists commonly treat otitis media (middle ear infection), and
Meniere's disease (disease of the middle ear that causes progressive
deafness). Otitis externa is an infection of the outer ear canal and can
occur at any age, ~~especially~~ *particularly* among swimmers.

Otits media is inflammation of the middle ear - the cavity between the
eardrum and the inner ear. There are three variations of this
inflammation: acute, chronic-secretory and chronic-suppurative.

This paragraph only in single-line spacing

Acute otitis media affects babies and very young children and the
symptoms are sudden earache, tinnitus (ringing or buzzing in the ear) and
a fever.

Chronic-suppurative otitis media is a persistent infection of the middle ear
affecting older children and adults.

Otits media is inflammation of the middle ear - the cavity between the
eardrum and the inner ear. There are three variations of this
inflammation: acute, chronic-secretory and chronic-suppurative.

Meniere's disease is a condition in which the body's balance mechanism in
the inner ear becomes swollen. In 85 per cent of cases only one ear is
affected. The main symptom is a sudden attack of vertigo with a
sensation of the room spinning round. The disease is caused by an
increase in the amount of fluid in the membranous labyrinth.

Chronic-secretory otitis media is most common among ~~ear~~ children aged five to seven years. It is also known as glue ear. The eustachian tube is blocked by the inflammation or sometimes by enlarged adenoids. Sometimes there is a feeling of dullness in the ear or even partial deafness.

The small bones of the ~~inner ear~~ middle ear as well as the eardrum are gradually damaged by the infection

The nose is the uppermost part of the respiratory tract and it is the organ
of smell. Sinus, a cavity within a bone, lined with mucous membrane
surrounding the nose. Mucus produced by this membrane drains into the
nasal cavity via narrow channels. Surgical drainage of affected sinuses is
a common operation in this department.

Otorhinolaryngology Exercise 6 continued

The throat is the passage running down from the back of the mouth and nose to the upper part of the oesophagus and the opening into the larynx. Tonsillectomy is the name for the surgical removal of the tonsils. With the patient under a general anaesthetic a tube is placed down the patient's wind pipe, (or trachea) to allow him or her to breathe during the operation. The tongue is depressed and the tonsils are/prised *then* from the back of the throat and cut away.

Pharyngeal cancer ◄——— *Emphasise this subheading*

Malignant tumours of the throat may be removed by surgery or treated with radiotherapy. Anti-cancer drugs may also be given. These tumours need early medical attention. They can occur in men or women and are most common in smokers. The highest incidence of pharyngeal cancer is in those who both smoke and drink alcohol.

Change throat to pharynx in the body of the text

Make sure all numbers are either figures or words — not a mix of both

Exam Practice

The Stage II Medical Word Processing Part 2 examination offered by RSA Examinations Board tests your ability to produce a variety of medical documents from handwritten and typewritten drafts.

You will be asked to produce four documents in one and three quarter hours. These are

- notice for display
- an article/report which contains a list of alphabetical and/or numerical/chronological information
- table
- a standard referral letter which includes phrases to be inserted from a stored file

In order to pass the examination you must complete the paper within the time given and incur no more than nine faults. If you incur only three faults or fewer, you will be awarded a distinction.

Three of the tasks in this examination include text that has previously been keyed in by your tutor – including saved phrases. The text and phrases which need to be keyed in for the purpose of the mock examination papers in this book can be found on pages 64–75.

Ensure the correct stationery is used – letters must be produced on letterheads and dated with the date of the examination. The letterheads for use with the mock examination papers can be found at the back of the book before the Glossary.

During the examination, you should:

- number continuation sheets for letters
- follow any instructions on layout, eg centring or rearranging text
- follow instructions for leaving horizontal or vertical space – in RSA examinations, measurements are given in millimetres only, so ensure your word processor is set to use metric measurements
- produce any extra copies that are required for letters – these may be additional printed copies or photocopies
- remember to indicate the routing of these extra copies – use a black pen to do this nearly
- include your name, centre number and document number on each piece of work, either at the top or bottom of every page – you might like to use the **Header** or **Footer** facility to do this
- ensure the top and left-hand margins are not less than 13mm
- ensure each printed sheet is clean and not creased, and
- assemble your completed work in the order in which it is presented within each exercise.

Note: Suggested answers for the mock examination papers in this book are displayed at the back of the book (pages 103–117).

Medical terms

The following is a list of medical terms that you will come across during the exam practice and an explanation of their meanings.

Amniocentesis	a procedure used for to diagnose genetic disorders in a fetus
Anaemia	a reduction of the ability of the blood to carry red blood cells
Antibiotic	a medicine derived from living organisms, usually bacteria or moulds, that kills microorganisms or reduces their growth
Antihistamine	a drug used to relieve the symptoms of allergies
Antiseptic	a chemical used to reduce the infectious growth of bacteria, viruses, and fungi
Antitetanus	an injection applied when a wound may be infected with tetanus (an acute and potentially fatal disease)
Appendix	a slender projection in the large intestine. Inflammation of an infected appendix is known as appendicitis
Constipation	difficulty or infrequency in evacuating the bowels
Diarrhoea	passage of frequent, more or less fluid material from the bowels, not a disease but a symptom of an underlying disorder
Diuretic	a chemical that increases the production of urine to help the body rid itself of excess fluids
Duodenum	part of the small intestine that further digests food
–ectomy	removal of an organ, for example appendicectomy is removal of the appendix
Endoscope	an instrument used for examining the inside of the body, also used for surgery
Enzyme	a protein molecule used by cells to speed up chemical processes
Epilepsy	a general term for brain disorders associated with convulsions and impaired consciousness
Fever	increased body temperature, a symptom of disease
Flexor	a muscle that, when contracted, bends a joint or limb
Haemoglobin	a red-pigmented protein found in red blood cells
Haemorrhoids (or piles)	distended veins usually filled with blood clots found around the anus
Haemostasis	stopping bleeding or preventing blood circulation, usually during an operation
Hydrocephalus	an accumulation of fluid inside the skull, usually resulting from an obstruction
Impetigo	a skin infection that occurs predominantly in children
Influenza (or flu)	an infectious disease caused by the influenza virus
Lymphatic system	the immune system of a body
Melanin	a skin pigment associated with darker skins
Migraine	a common type of headache, felt on only one side of the body
–natal	referring to birth, for example antenatal means before birth
Neuralgia	a disorder of the nervous system, involving sudden pain without inflammation
Neurophysiology	the study of the structure and function of the nervous system
Placenta	an organ that filters oxygen and food from the mother to the fetus through the umbilical cord
Psoriasis	a common skin disease

Rheumatism	a term for several diseases that affect joints, muscles, ligaments or tendons, such as arthritis or lumbago
Sedative	a drug used either for a calming effect or to produce sleep
Spina bifida	a birth defect where part of the spinal cord is left exposed
Stenosis	narrowing of a passage in the body
Suture	a surgical stitch *or* an immovable joint
Trichomonas	a type of parasitic microorganism
Ulcer	an erosion or disintegration of tissues, which can be on the skin or mucous surfaces. Ulcers of the gastrointestinal tract are called peptic ulcers
Ulnar nerve	a nerve on the inner side of the arm near the elbow

Recalled text

Two of the documents in the Stage II Medical Word Processing examination will be recalled from previously saved files for you to make amendments as instructed. Additionally, one of the documents will require you to copy previously stored documents to specified locations within a separate document.

The files and phrases you will need for the mock examination papers in this book should be typed exactly as shown in the draft documents which follow. Some of the documents require you to key in text with deliberate errors for you to correct when the files are recalled – these are circled. To undertake these mock papers under examination conditions, key in the passages as shown (including the errors).

Although one of the documents requires you to copy part of a recalled file, the whole document should be keyed in to test your ability to recall part of a previously stored document.

Save all the files under the file name given but do not print a copy.

In the examination, the recalled text will be keyed in by your tutor in advance. However, when working through this book, use these documents to practise your keyboarding and accuracy skills.

Exam Practice 1 Recalled Text 1

Key in the following document exactly as shown except for line endings and page breaks, which must be allowed to occur naturally. Use single-line spacing and a ragged right-hand margin. Ensure a line length of a) 16.5cm or b) 65 characters. If proportional spacing is used, please ensure a line length of a). Circled text indicates a deliberate error which must be typed *as shown* (do not correct error). Save as HERB1.

HERBAL MEDICINE

From the earliest of times, herbs have been used for their healing abilities and for pain relief. We still rely on the curative properties of plants in about 75 per cent of our medicines today. Societies around the world have developed their own traditions concerning medicinal plants and their uses.

Most commonly used herbs are extremely safe to use. A few plants can have side-effects for some people. Like all medicines, herbal remedies must be treated with respect. A well-trained practitioner will help and give guidance. Ephredra is an evergreen shrub with long, narrow stems and tiny leaves. It is used principally as a treatment for asthma, hay fever and for the acute onset of colds and influenza.

It can help to raise bloodpressure, cool fever and alleviate rheumatism. Whilst it can help all these ailments, it can also be extremely toxic when taken at the wrong dosage.

Throughout the world, thousands of plant species have medicinal uses. They contain active constituents that have a direct action on the body. They are used in both herbal and conventional medicines offering benefits that pharmaceutical drugs cannot. Herbal medicine often compliments conventional treatments. They can provide safe remedies for chronic illnesses.

Depending on the chemical constituents that a herbal medicine contains, the body is affected in different ways. Research is still being undertaken plant constituents. Plants contain hundreds of different constituents that interact in complex ways.

Good health depends on having a balanced nervous system. Long term good health of the nervous system requires one to look at the demands of life. Excessive anxiety, worry or depression should be avoided.

Many herbs work with the immune, nervous and endocrine systems and they are effective because they work in line with the body's processes. Ginseng has oval, toothed leaves and clusters of green-yellow flowers. This herb is an adaptogenic, it can help people to adapt, by supporting the nervous system. It can be an effective remedy at times of great men tal or physical stress.

A way of classifying medicinal plants is to identify their action - whether they are sedative, antiseptic, or diuretic and the way they affect the body differently.

A herb is a complex natural medicine composed of mainly active constituents that work on different parts of the body systems.

Exam Practice 1 Recalled Text 2

Key in the following document exactly as shown except for line endings, which must be allowed to occur naturally. Save as HERB2.

The Medicinal Herb Garden

When planning a herb garden take into account the amount of space available, soil conditions and climate. Choose a range of hardy herbs that will establish themselves quickly and produce an abundance of foliage that can be harvested.

Lemon balm
Fever few
Marigold
Rosemary
Peppermint
Thyme
Sage
St John's wort

Cultivated herb gardens create an aromatic, colourful area providing fresh herbs to use medicinally and in cooking.

Exam Practice 1 Recalled Text 4

Key in the following phrases and save as shown. Do not key in the phrase numbers as part of the recalled text – they are shown for identification purposes only.

Phrase 1 (Save as HERB3).

We discussed taking agnus castus tablets as research has shown that the berries have a very distinct hormonal effect on the body. Chinese angelica could be used as a uterine tonic to help infertility.

Phrase 2 (Save as HERB4).

I have prescribed her a course of agnus castus tablets as these will help her low progesterone level, and have made an appointment to see her again in 6 weeks' time.

Phrase 3 (Save as HERB5).

Herbal/Homeopathy Clinic
Himiyah Kasan MNIMH
Medical Herbalist

HK/your initials/MH47229

Dr A J Wright
The Liberty Health Centre
The Liberty
WELLS
BA5 2FX

Exam Practice 2 Recalled Text 1

Key in the following document exactly as shown except for line endings and page breaks, which must be allowed to occur naturally. Use single-line spacing and a ragged right-hand margin. Ensure a line length of a) 16cm or b) 65 characters. If proportional spacing is used, please ensure a line length of a). Circled text indicates a deliberate error which must be typed as shown (do not correct error). Save as OBSTET1.

SOME FACTS ABOUT PREGNANCY

OBSTETRICS

During pregnancy a single microscopic cell develops into a fully grown baby containing in excess of 6 million cells. A human being grows more rapidly in the womb than at any other time.

A typical pregnancy lasts from 38 to 40 weeks and this is counted from the first day of the last menstrual bleeding. This period of time can be broken into three parts - 0 to 12 weeks, 13 to 28 weeks and 29 to 40 weeks.

The first most obvious sign of pregnancy is a lack of menstrual bleeding. Changes in the body start by the breasts starting to swell and becoming tender as the mammary glands develop. A supportive bra should be worn. There is an urge to pass urine more frequently and often a white discharge(fromthe)vagina. Nausea and vomiting, particularly in the morning, are very common symptoms.

From 16 weeks the enlarging uterus is easily felt. Some females may have a warm, flushed feeling. They may have an increased appetite together with a gain in weight. Feelings of nausea and frequency to pass urine usually cease between 13 to 28 weeks, and the woman may feel generally better, with more energy than she did in the earlier weeks.

At this time a woman's heart rate increases. This is to allow the fetus to develop properly. For some females stretch-marks develop on the abdomen, breasts and thighs during the final weeks.

In a first pregnancy the baby's head drops down low into the pelvis at about week 36. In subsequent pregnancies this is usually later.

Some minor problems that can occur during pregnancy are constipation, haemorrhoids, heartburn and a craving to eat(sub stances)such as clay or coal. Varicose veins, swollen ankles, leg cramps and(headache)are also common during late pregnancy. Urinary tract infections and stress incontinence may occur in the later weeks.

The average weight increase in pregnancy is 12.7 kg. Seventy per cent of this occurs during the last 20 weeks. At full term a typical fetus would weigh 3.4 kg, the placenta and fluid together 1.4 kg, leaving the rest of the weight to be water retention.

Exam Practice 2 Recalled Text 2

Key in the following document exactly as shown except for line endings, which must be allowed to occur naturally. Save as OBSTET2.

THE LIBERTY HEALTH CENTRE

Antenatal Clinic

Our clinics are held each week on a Tuesday and Thursday morning. After your initial visit, you should attend once a month until the 28th week, every two weeks until the 36th week and then weekly until the 40th week (your delivery date).

2   advice on exercise and diet
6   postnatal period
1   what happens during labour
4   pain relief available
3   breathing exercises
5   relaxation techniques

An insight will be given concerning postnatal care. Temperature, blood pressure and pulse will be monitored regularly.

Exam Practice 2 Recalled Text 4

Key in the following phrases and save as shown. Do not key in the phrase numbers as part of the recalled text – they are shown for identification purposes only.

Phrase 1 (Save as OBSTET3).

The cervical smear that was taken by your clinic was negative. The vaginal swab taken showed pus cells but there was no growth on culture.

Phrase 2 (Save as OBSTET4).

Checks will be made for stenosis, trichomonas and any malignant cells.

Yours sincerely

Mr Edward Hutton FRCS
Senior Gynaecologist

Phrase 3 (Save as OBSTET5).

Senior Gynaecologist
Mr Edward Hutton FRCS

EH/your initials/ANC498

Dr A J Wright
The Liberty Health Centre
The Liberty
WELLS
BA5 2FX

Exam Practice 3 Recalled Text 1

Key in the following document exactly as shown except for line endings and page breaks, which must be allowed to occur naturally. Use single-line spacing and a ragged right-hand margin. Ensure a line length of 16.5cm. Circled text indicates a deliberate error which must be typed *as shown* (do not correct error). Save as GASTRO1.

GASTROENTEROLOGY

Gastroenterology is the study of the digestive system and a specialist in this branch of medicine is called a gastroenterologist. He or she treats patients by advising on diet and lifestyle, prescribing medication when necessary and referring patients for surgical treatment, for example appendicitis.

Digestion starts when food enters the mouth, is broken down and chewed by the teeth and then the salivary glands secrete saliva to lubricate it. The saliva also contains enzymes that break down the starches. The mouth also contains sensory nerves. The tongue (which contains taste buds) manipulates the food into small balls, called bolus ready for easy swallowing.

The digestive system is the group of organs consisting of the alimentary canal which forms a continuous passage from the mouth to the anus, and various other associated organs. This group of organs breaks down food into the various chemical components that the body can absorb and use for energy. These components, starches, sugar, fats, proteins, minerals and vitamins, are also used to build and repair body cells and tissues.

From the mouth (thefood) passes without changing, through the pharynx, and into the oesophagus. Peristalsis, waves of muscular contractions, carries the food down the oesophagus to the stomach. Hydrochloric acid and (pep sin) from the stomach lining helps to break down proteins. The continual churning action of the stomach mechanically turns the food into a semi-fluid mass called chyme. This is then released into the duodenum.

Whilst passing through the duodenum, the food is broken down further by enzymes from the pancreas. These enzymes further break down starches, protein and fats.

The duodenum leads into the small intestine and here, additional enzymes produced by glands in the lining complete the food breakdown.

Nutrients are absorbed by the thin lining of the intestine into the bloodstream and lymphatic system.

The final stage is for the food residue to pass through the large intestine, where much of the water is absorbed through the lining of the colon. Undigested residue then passes into the rectum and anus ready to be expelled.

The digestive tract is very tolerant of what is passed through it but it reacts strongly against infected foods, poisons and other irritants causing vomiting or diaorrhea. Indigestion is a very common disorder.

Exam Practice 3 Recalled Text 2

Key in the following document exactly as shown except for line endings, which must be allowed to occur naturally. Save as GASTRO2.

QUANTOCK DISTRICT HOSPITAL

Recruitment drive for Staff Nurses Grade E in the Gastroenterology Wards.

caring and dedicated staff
job satisfaction
promotional opportunities
friendly and dynamic team
in-house learning opportunities
paid study leave

In addition to the above there will be information on:

TRAINING

AMENITIES

SALARY

The use of endoscopes has meant that many major operations are now only minor ones. The gastroscope is a flexible fibre-optic endoscope and is used to check disorders of the oesophagus, stomach and duodenum.

For further information please contact:

Mrs Amara Aluko
Quantock District Hospital

Exam Practice 3 Recalled Text 4

Key in the following phrases and save as shown. Do not key in the phrase numbers as part of the recalled text – they are shown for identification purposes only.

Phrase 1 (Save as GASTRO3).

Mr Smith said that he had suffered from heartburn for a number of years. He is not overweight for his height. He thought the burning pain he had felt in his chest had now moved down.

Phrase 2 (Save as GASTRO4).

Please refer him to me without an appointment if the matter becomes urgent.

Yours sincerely

Mr G W Martin MRCS
Consultant Gastroenterologist

Phrase 3 (Save as GASTRO5).

                                        Consultant Gastroenterologist
                                        Mr G W Martin MRCS

GWM/your initials/47549

Dr W Broadstone
The Liberty Health Centre
The Liberty
WELLS
BA5 2FX

Exam Practice 4 Recalled Text 1

Key in the following document exactly as shown except for line endings and page breaks, which must be allowed to occur naturally. Use single-line spacing and a ragged right-hand margin. Ensure a line length of a) 16.5cm or b) 65 characters. If proportional spacing is used, please ensure a line length of a). Circled text indicates a deliberate error which must be typed *as shown* (do not correct error). Save as DERMA1.

DERMATOLOGY

THE SKIN AND SOME DISORDERS

The skin's main function is a protective one. It is vulnerable to minor injury. It shields the internal organs of the body from injury, harmful sunlight and bacteria. It is the body's largest organ and through wear and tear cells are continually being replaced.

Skin forms the outermost covering of the body tissue. It varies in thickness from 0.05 mm to 5 mm with the thinnest skin being found on the eyelid to the thickest on the sole of the foot or palm of the hand.

The structure of skin consists of an outer layer of cells, the epidermis, a thicker inner layer, the dermis, and a deeper subcutaneous layer which contains fat.

Hair and nails are extensions of the skin. They are composed mainly of keratin, which is one of a family of proteins that also make up a major constituent of the outer layer of the epidermis. Most of the cells in the epidermis are specialised to produce keratin and some of the cells produce melanin. Melanocytes cells are at the base of the hair roots. The dermis contains blood vessels, lymph vessels and nerves. In the deeper parts of the dermis are hair roots, sweat glands and sebaceous glands. The sebaceous glands produce a protective, oily substance called sebum. This provides a thin film of fat over the skin and nourishes the hair roots.

The epidermis is water proof and the outermost part of the epidermis has a protective coating and water-holding capacity. This all helps to maintain the body balance of fluid and electrolytes. Skin becomes cracked if the water level drops below a certain level.

Main symptoms of skin disorder are

rash
lumps
itching
skin abnormalities

Skin disorders are seldom life-threatening, but they can cause distress to the sufferer often leading to psychological problems.

Diagnosis of most skin disorders canbe taken from the physical characteristic of the disorder. Diagnosis by the removal of skin tissue for microscopic analysis (skin biopsy) is usually taken to exclude skin cancer problems.

Viral infections and inflammation of the skin are cold sores and warts. Bacterial infections include boils and impetigo, whilst common fungal infections include athlete's foot and tinea (ringworm).

Exam Practice 4 Recalled Text 2

Key in the following document exactly as shown except for line endings, which must be allowed to occur naturally. Save as DERMA2.

Atopic Eczema

Eczema is an inflammation of the skin, causing itching and red scaly skin. Atopic eczema is common in babies and young children.

2   cutting finger nails short
6   keeping away from household pets
1   dressing in loose cotton clothing
4   swimming in the sea
3   avoiding biological washing powders
5   limiting intake of milk, eggs and cheese

Small red pimples appear on the scaling skin and as the child scratches the pimples they ooze and form crusts.

Atopic eczema is not infectious. It cannot be passed from one person to another.

Exam Practice 4 Recalled Text 3

Key in the following phrases and save as shown. Do not key in the phrase numbers as part of the recalled text – they are shown for identification purposes only.

Phrase 1 (Save as DERMA3).

After a thorough examination I found no other traces of psoriasis on his body, although he did have patches of dry skin on his elbows. He has had no recent physical illness and has not been under any emotional stress.

Phrase 2 (Save as DERMA4).

He has been advised to wear non-irritating materials, such as cotton, next to his skin.

Phrase 3 (Save as DERMA5).

Dermatology Department
Miss Christine Tsang
Dermatologist

CT/your initials/9854239

Dr S Khan
The Liberty Health Centre
The Liberty
WELLS
BA5 2FX

Exam Practice 5 Recalled Text 1

Key in the following document exactly as shown except for line endings and page breaks, which must be allowed to occur naturally. Use single-line spacing and a ragged right-hand margin. Ensure a line length of a) 16.5cm or b) 65 characters. If proportional spacing is used, please ensure a line length of a). Circled text indicates a deliberate error which must be typed *as shown* (do not correct error). Save as NEURO1.

NEUROLOGY AND NEUROSURGERY

Neurology is the study of the nervous system, its diseases and malfunction. The nervous system is divided into two main areas; the central nervous system and the autonomic nervous system. The central nervous system comprises the brain and the spinal cord, which consists of billions of interconnecting nerve cells (neurons).

Sense organs pass input to the central nervous system. These include physical feeling such as pain, touch, heat and cold. The motor nerves instruct the body to react in certain ways. For example, the sweat glands work when it is hot.

The main function of the nervous system is to gather information about conditions inside and outside the body. The central nervous system analyses this information. The most powerful drive we have is for survival. The nervous system initiates unconsciously the drive to avoid physical pain and it responds to cold by shivering.

The autonomic part of the nervous system consists of two particular groups of nerves - the sympathetic and the parasympathetic. The primary concern of the sympathetic system is to prepare the body for action. It stimulates functions such as heart rate, blood pressure and the circulation of blood to the limbs. The parasympathetic system has the opposite effect, it slows down the heart rate.

The two systems act in conjunction and so maintain the fine balance needed. During times of exercise the sympathetic (isthe)predominating system, whilst the parasympathetic system has more control during sleep.

Neurosurgery is concerned with the surgical treatment of disorders of the brain, spinal cord and other parts of the nervous system. These disorders include tumours and abnormalities of the blood vessels that supply the brain. Some birth defects such as spina bifida and hydrocephalus are other disorders. Brain abscesses and intracerebral haemorrhage, certain types of epilepsy, and nerve damage caused by accidents or illness are all disorders that are treated by neurosurgeons. Some of the main symptoms of a nervous disorder are:

convulsion
unconsciousness
tremble
headache

Parkinson's disease is a neurological disorder that causes muscle tremble, (stiff ness) and weakness. A slight tremble in one hand is usually the first sign of the disease. It is caused by either degeneration of or damage to nerve cells in the basal ganglia in the brain. The basal ganglia (paired nerve cell clusters) play a very important part in producing smooth muscular actions.

Levodopa is usually the most efficient drug.

Exam Practice 5 Recalled Text 2

Key in the following document exactly as shown except for line endings, which must be allowed to occur naturally. Save as NEURO2.

QUANTOCK DISTRICT HOSPITAL

CONFERENCE ON PARKINSON'S DISEASE AND PARKINSONISM

1 General introduction
4 Update on the use of physiotherapy
3 Dietary aspects of management
5 Neurophysiology of swallowing
2 Concepts of managing a chronic disease
7 The way forward
6 Specialist nurses impact

FORMAT

COST

AIMED AT

As our population ages, Parkinson's disease becomes more and more prevalent. About one in every 200 people has the disease and it is more common in men than women.

A complete programme with application form will be mailed to all interested parties nearer the time.

Exam Practice 5 Recalled Text 4

Key in the following phrases and save as shown. Do not key in the phrase numbers as part of the recalled text – they are shown for identification purposes only.

Phrase 1 (Save as NEURO3).

The wound was very clean when you performed the surgery, and the mattress method of suturing was the correct type to use for a deep wound.

Phrase 2 (Save as NEURO4).

She has been prescribed a course of Cloxacillin, an antibacterial and antibiotic drug.

Yours sincerely

Mrs Helen McCallum
Consultant Neurologist

Phrase 3 (Save as NEURO5).

Neurological Clinic
Mrs Helen McCallum
Consultant Neurologist

HMcC/your initials/171/4379

Dr S Khan
The Liberty Health Centre
The Liberty
WELLS
BA5 2FX

3

Exam Practice 1 Document 1

Insert NATURAL CURES AND THE METABOLISM as a header on every page

Change the word body to metabolism throughout this document

HERBAL MEDICINE

[copy this paragraph] *(A)* 10

From the earliest of times, herbs have been used for their healing abilities and for pain relief. We still rely on the curative properties of plants in about 75 per cent of our medicines today. ~~Societies around the world have developed their own traditions concerning medicinal plants and their uses.~~

(B)

Most commonly used herbs are extremely safe to use. A few plants can have side-effects for some people. Like all medicines, herbal remedies must be treated with respect. A well-trained practitioner will help and give guidance. *[be able to]* Ephredra is an evergreen shrub with long, narrow stems and tiny leaves. It is used principally as a treatment for asthma, hay fever and for the acute onset of colds and influenza.

It can help to raise blood pressure, cool fever and alleviate rheumatism. Whilst it can help all these ailments, it can also be extremely toxic when taken at the wrong dosage.

[Move this paragraph to (B)]

Throughout the world, thousands of plant species have medicinal uses. They contain active constituents that have a direct action on the body. ~~They~~ *These constituents* are used in both herbal and conventional medicines offering benefits that pharmaceutical drugs ~~cannot~~ *often lack*. Herbal medicine often compliments conventional treatments. They can provide safe remedies for chronic illnesses.

Depending on the chemical constituents that a herbal medicine contains, the body is affected in different ways. Research is still being undertaken *into* plant constituents. Plants contain hundreds of different constituents that interact in complex ways.

[leave at least 25mm here]

Good health depends on having a balanced nervous system. Long term good health of the nervous system ~~requires~~ one to look at the demands of life. Excessive anxiety, worry or depression should be avoided. *Dosages must be carefully followed.*

The nervous system is linked with the endocrine system which controls the release of hormones. It is also linked with the immune system. This system controls the resistance to infection and recovery from

illness and injury. This complex of systems, part
electrical, part chemical and part mechanical must
function in harmony if good health is to be
maintained.

This paragraph only in single line spacing

Many herbs work with the immune, nervous and endocrine systems and they are
effective because they work in line with the body's processes. Ginseng has oval,
toothed leaves and clusters of green-yellow flowers. This herb is an adaptogenic, it
can help people to adapt, by supporting the nervous system. It can be an effective
remedy at times of great mental or physical stress.

A way of classifying medicinal plants is to identify their action - whether they are
sedative, antiseptic, or diuretic and the way they affect the body differently.

~~A herb is a complex natural medicine composed of mainly active constituents that
work on different parts of the body systems~~.

It also can be taken when a relaxing
effect is required, for example to
get a good night's rest, or to
relieve a headache.

Exam Practice 1 Document 2

Recall this document stored as HERB2. Amend as shown. Save as HERB7 and print one copy.

The Medicinal Herb Garden ← *Emphasise this heading*

When planning a herb garden take into account the amount of space available, soil conditions and climate. Choose a range of hardy herbs that will establish themselves quickly and produce an abundance of foliage that can be harvested.

The following plants should grow well:

Lemon balm
Fever few
Marigold
Rosemary
Peppermint
Thyme
Sage
St John's wort

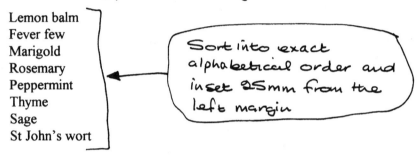

Sort into exact alphabetical order and inset 25mm from the left margin

Some medicinal plants can be grown in

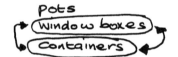

pots
Window boxes
Containers

or even hanging baskets. Bay laurel is an ideal plant for growing in a container but care must be taken to prevent it from drying out or becoming pot-bound.

There is a wide variety of propagation methods including seeds, cuttings, root division and layering. Taking cuttings is the most popular method. Cuttings are usually taken from the stem but some may be taken from the roots. Do not feed or mulch medicinal herbs as this reduces their therapeutic strength.

Cultivated herb gardens create an aromatic, colourful area providing fresh herbs to use medicinally and in cooking.

Centre this section

Exam Practice 1 Document 3

key in the following table. Save as HERB8 and print one
copy. Do not rule the table.

QUANTOCK DISTRICT HOSPITAL

HERBAL | HOMEOPATHIC DEPARTMENT

Check the name of this
herb from Document 2
and amend if necessary

Listed below are the stock numbers of herbal treatments
we keep for use with the more common ailments we come
across at our monthly clinic.

COMMON AILMENT	STOCK NUMBER	GENERAL REMEDIES	
		HERB USED	REMEDY

Nerve and stress related problems

Common Ailment	Stock Number	Herb Used	Remedy
Sinus headache	48	Lime flowers	Teabag infusion
Migraine headache	45	Rosemary leaves	50ml infusion
Neuralgia	47	St David's Wort	Infused oil
Toothache	51	Dried clove	Chew a clove
Insomnia	52	Hops	Tincture with water

Reproductive, pregnancy and menstrual problems

Common Ailment	Stock Number	Herb Used	Remedy
Fluid retention	84	Dandelion	Leaf infusion
Pre-menstrual tension	81	Valerian	Tablets or tincture
Fertility problems (women)	92	Agnus castus	Tablets or tincture
Nausea and sickness	85	Fennel	Seed infusion
Haemorrhoids	96	Witch hazel bark	Ointment
Decreased oestrogen	97	Helonias root	Tablets

Digestive disorders

Common Ailment	Stock Number	Herb Used	Remedy
Stomach spasm	52	Chamomile	Flowerhead infusion
Acidity and indigestion	54	Slippery elm	Bark infusion
Diarrhoea	55	Agrimony	Decoction of herb
Constipation	57	Yellow dock	Root decoction
Mouth and tongue ulcers	58	Myrrh resin	Tincture or powder

Please sort into exact
numerical order of
STOCK NUMBER
within each
section

Please modify layout so that
REMEDY column appears to the
left of HERB USED column

Please modify layout so that
Digestive disorders is above
Nerve and stress related
problems

Exam Practice 1 Document 4

> Please key in the following document and insert the phrases as indicated. Save as HERB9 and print.

> Insert Phrase 3 stored as HERB5

Dear Dr Wright

Re   Ms Lavinia Rushton   DOB   19/12/75
        Mendip Cottage   Coxley   WELLS   BA5 7WP

This lady was seen today at the above clinic. As you know she would like to become pregnant by her partner but she is having difficulty in conceiving.

As this was her first visit we discussed her family traits, diet, lifestyle and any anxieties or stress she may have. I gave her a physical examination. I have also sent her urine for analysis and a blood test was taken to measure her haemoglobin level.

Her menstrual cycle is regular and she stopped taking the progestogen-only oral contraceptive pill six months ago. She is not overweight and she exercises regularly, mainly by having a brisk walk whilst out with her dogs.

In her work situation she has a small amount of stress, but this together with her failing to conceive is building up her stress and anxiety levels. We discussed the importance of a well-balanced diet, exercise and time for relaxation. I have suggested she would benefit from attending the Yoga exercise classes organised by the Cardiology Department.

> Insert Phrase 2 stored as HERB4

Yours sincerely

Himiyah Kasan
Medical Herbalist

> Top plus 2 please.
> One file copy and one for Dr Jordanna Cutajar.
> Indicate routing.

Exam Practice 2 Document 1

Change the word females to women throughout this document

Insert GROWTH CYCLE to appear as a header on every page

SOME FACTS ABOUT PREGNANCY

OBSTETRICS

Copy this paragraph to (A)

During pregnancy a single microscopic cell develops into a fully grown baby containing in excess of 6 million cells. A human being grows more rapidly in the womb than at any other time.

A typical pregnancy lasts from 38 to 40 weeks and this is counted from the first day of the last menstrual bleeding. This period of time can be broken into 3 parts - 0 to 12 weeks, 13 to 28 weeks and 29 to 40 weeks.

Move this paragraph to (B)

The first most obvious sign of pregnancy is a lack of menstrual bleeding. Changes in the body start by the breasts ~~starting to~~ *beginning* swell and becoming tender as the mammary glands develop. ~~A supportive bra should be worn~~. There is an urge to pass urine more frequently and often a white discharge from the vagina. Nausea and vomiting, particularly in the morning, are very common symptoms.

(B)

In the first 4 weeks since conception the egg develops to approximately 3mm in length. After 6 weeks it grows to approximately 25mm and the embryo inside it measures almost 10mm long. ~~*During this time the*~~ *By 8 weeks the embryo has most of its organs.* ~~*major organs are developing.*~~ *It is during the first 12 weeks of pregnancy that the growing baby is most vulnerable to damage.*

(leave at least 25mm here)

The enlarging uterus can easily be felt at 16 weeks.
~~From 16 weeks the enlarging uterus is easily felt.~~ Some females may have a warm, flushed feeling. They may have an increased appetite together with a gain in weight. Feelings of nausea and frequency to pass urine usually cease between 13 to 28 weeks, and the woman may feel generally better, with more energy than she did in the earlier weeks.

For the first 8 weeks the developing baby is called an embryo and after that time a fetus.

and volume of blood pumped to the heart

At this time a woman's heart rate increases. ▼This is to allow the fetus to develop properly. [For some females stretch-marks develop on the abdomen, breasts and thighs during the final weeks. ⌐

In a first pregnancy the baby's head drops down low into the pelvis at about week 36. In subsequent pregnancies this is usually later.

This paragraph only is single line spacing

Some minor problems that can occur during pregnancy are constipation, haemorrhoids, heartburn and a craving to eat substances such as clay or coal. Varicose veins, swollen ankles, leg cramps and headache are also common during late pregnancy. ~~Urinary tract infections and stress incontinence may occur in the later weeks~~.

The average weight increase in pregnancy is 12.7 kg. Seventy per cent of this occurs during the last 20 weeks. At full term a typical fetus would weigh 3.4 kg, the placenta and fluid together 1.4 kg, leaving the rest of the weight to be ~~water~~ retention.

This can put a strain on the heart of females with existing heart disorders.

Recall this document stored as OBSTET2
Amend as shown. Save as OBSTET7   and print
one copy.

THE LIBERTY HEALTH CENTRE

Antenatal Clinic ← Emphasise this heading

Our clinics are held each week on a Tuesday and Thursday morning. After your initial
visit, you should attend once a month until the 28th week, every two weeks until the
36th week and then weekly until the 40th week (your delivery date).

Your first visit to the clinic is the most thorough
and the longest. A midwife will take a small sample
of blood to be examined for anaemia and folic acid
deficiency and to check your blood group. A urine
test for proteinuria will also be taken and your
blood pressure will be checked for hypertension.

You will be invited to attend childbirth preparation
classes, when information is given on the following

2 advice on exercise and diet
6 postnatal period
1 what happens during labour
4 pain relief available
3 breathing exercises
5 relaxation techniques

Sort into exact numerical
order and inset 25mm
from the left margin

An insight will be given concerning postnatal care. Temperature, blood pressure and
pulse will be monitored regularly. Instruction on pelvic floor
exercises to restore muscle tone will also be given.

Centre this section

Exam Practice 2 Document 3

Key in the following table. Same as OBSTET8 and print one copy. Do not rule the table.

THE LIBERTY HEALTH SURGERY

Check this word from Document 2 and amend if necessary

Antenatal clinic details for patients who may have some problems throughout their pregnancy.

Mention's Sentence so that it comes above PATIENT'S NAME

PATIENT'S NAME	DAY	GENERAL DESCRIPTION PROCEDURE/CONCERN	TIME OF APPOINTMENT
First visit to clinic			
DAVIES Melanie	Tuesday	Cervical smear, no recent test	0900
HOUSTON Greta	Tuesday	Blood test for hepatitis B	0930
HALIDAY Gemma	Thursday	Blood test for anaemia	1100
HARRISON Hayley	Thursday	Urine test for proteinuria	1130
SIMPSON Diana	Tuesday	Blood test to check group	1500
12 week visit to clinic			
CROSS Suk kam	Thursday	Raised blood pressure	0900
GRAY Kirsty	Thursday	Severe vomiting	0930
HODGE Erica	Thursday	Raised blood pressure	1000
HENVILLE Jodie	Tuesday	Swollen ankles	1000
FLYNN Paula	Tuesday	Blood test for Rubella	1030
WILLIAMS Helen	Tuesday	Unexplained weight gain	1100
16-18 week visit to clinic			
BUCKLE Marcia	Thursday	Amniocentesis for spina bifida	1030
KNOX Jessica	Thursday	Fetoscopy for fetal disorder	1100
LAMB Amy	Tuesday	Amniocentesis for spina bifida	1030
ROBERTS Dalta	Tuesday	Blood test for anaemia	1100
STONE Carol	Thursday	Fetoscopy for fetal disorder	1130

After their consultation here, these patients will need to be referred to Dr Nicola Heritage.

Please sort into exact alphabetical order by PATIENT SURNAME within each section

Please modify layout so that TIME OF APPOINTMENT appears to the left of PROCEDURE/CONCERN column

Please key in the following document and insert the phrases as indicated. Save as OBSTET9 and print.

Insert Phrase 3 stored as OBSTET5

Dear Dr Wright

Re Mrs Heather Yeomans   DOB   18/05/68
   29 South Parade   Dinder   WELLS   BA5 5UJ

I saw the above-named lady again in the Outpatients Department this morning. She is still complaining of a vaginal discharge. The discharge started after the birth of her second child. This was in 1997 when she gave birth to a normal full term male infant, weight 3.5 kg. She had a postnatal examination at 14 weeks when she complained of an irritant discharge.

Her menstrual cycle is regular with no intermenstrual bleeding. She has no adverse urinary or bowel symptoms. On examination her vagina and vulva were found to be healthy, but the cervix appeared to be congested with the discharge.

I will make arrangements for her to be admitted when a diathermy of the cervix under a general anaesthetic will be performed. The diseased area will be removed and haemostasis with electro-coagulation will take place.

Insert Phrase 2 stored as OBSTET4

Yours sincerely

Mr Edward Hutton FRCS
Senior Gynaecologist

Top plus 2 please. One file copy and one for Dr Nicola Heritage Indicate routing.

Exam Practice 3 Document 1

Change the word
Starches to
carbohydrates
throughout
this document

Insert The Digestive System
to appear as a footer on
every page

GASTROENTEROLOGY

Copy this paragraph to (A)

Gastroenterology is the study of the digestive system and a specialist in this branch of
medicine is called a gastroenterologist. He or she treats patients by advising on diet
and lifestyle, prescribing medication when necessary and referring patients for surgical
treatment, for example appendicitis. ~~ectomy~~.

(B)

• It is

Digestion starts when food enters the mouth, is broken down and chewed by the teeth
and then the salivary glands secrete saliva to lubricate it. The saliva also contains
enzymes that break down the starches. ~~The mouth also contains sensory nerves~~. The
tongue (which contains taste buds) manipulates the food into small balls, called bolus
ready for easy swallowing.

Move this paragraph to (B)

The digestive system is the group of organs consisting of the alimentary canal which
forms a continuous passage from the mouth to the anus, and various other ~~other~~ ~~associated~~ ✓
organs. This group of organs breaks down food into the various chemical components
that the body can absorb and use for energy. These components, starches, sugar, fats,
proteins, minerals and vitamins, are also used to build and repair body cells and tissues.

From the mouth the food passes without changing, through the pharynx, and into the
oesophagus. Peristalsis, waves of muscular contractions, carries the food down the
oesophagus to the stomach. Hydrochloric acid and pepsin from the stomach lining
helps to break down proteins. The continual churning action of the stomach
in the food
mechanically turns the food into a semi-fluid mass called chyme. This is then released
into the duodenum.

Whilst passing through the duodenum, the food is broken down further by enzymes
from the pancreas. These enzymes further break down starches, protein and fats.

The duodenum leads into the small intestine and here, additional enzymes produced by
glands in the lining complete the ~~food breakdown~~. final breakdown of the food.

Nutrients are absorbed by the thin lining of the intestine into the bloodstream and
lymphatic system.

bile salts and acids produced
by the liver and released from
the gall bladder and

Exam Practice 3 Document 1 continued

The final stage is for the food residue to pass through the large intestine, where much of the water is absorbed through the lining of the colon. Undigested residue then *and dehydrated* passes into the rectum and anus ready to be expelled.

This paragraph is a single linespacing

Food spends the following approximate time going through the digestive system. One minute breaking the food down in the mouth followed by 10 seconds in the oesophagus. It is in the stomach between 2 and 4 hours and the small intestine for 1 to 6 hours. It can be in the large intestine from 10 hours up to several days.

The digestive tract is very tolerant of what is passed through it but it reacts strongly against infected foods, poisons and other irritants causing vomiting or diaorrhea. ~~Indigestion is a very common disorder~~.

leave space here of at least 50mm

(A)

Exam Practice 3 Document 2

Recall this document stored as GASTRO2. Amend as shown. Save as GASTRO4 and print one copy.

QUANTOCK DISTRICT HOSPITAL

Recruitment drive for Staff Nurses Grade E in the Gastroenterology Wards.

The following is a summary of what will be on the information sheet we send out to prospective applicants.

caring and dedicated staff
job satisfaction
promotional opportunities
friendly and dynamic team
in-house learning opportunities
paid study leave

Sort into exact alphabetical order and inset 25mm from the left margin

In addition to the above there will be information on:

TRAINING

*Travel scholarship
ENB998 and A24 funding*

AMENITIES

*Hospital accommodation
Subsidised canteen
Licensed social club
Tennis courts*

SALARY

*£14,191 – £16,440
working 37½ hours per week*

We also have an on-site nursery, a counselling service and fully equipped library.

The use of endoscopes has meant that many major operations are now only minor ones. The gastroscope is a flexible fibre-optic endoscope and is used to check disorders of the oesophagus, stomach and duodenum.

Experience of assisting with the work involving endoscopes is necessary for this post. The position will also involve the care of patients and their relatives from admission to discharge.

Emphasise this sentence

For further information please contact:

Mrs Amara Aluko
Quantock District Hospital
County Bridge Road
TAUNTON
TA1 7AB

Centre this section

Exam Practice 3 Document 3

Key in the following table. Save as GASTRO 8 and print one copy. Do not rule the table.

QUANTOCK DISTRICT HOSPITAL
List of patients in the Gastrectomy Wards to have operations/treatment this week.

Check this word from document 2 and amend if necessary

NAME OF PATIENT	TIME OF OPERATION	OPERATION REASON	DIAGNOSIS OPERATION/TREATMENT
Tuesday – Surgeon Mr Senior			
Sophie MADSEN	1000	Appendicitis	Appendicectomy
Michaela YEE	0900	Ulcer	Anal fissure
Carolyn WOOD	1030	Haemorrhoids	Haemorrhoidectomy
Diane McKENZIE	1130	Tumour	Pancreatectomy
Tara HENDERSON	1100	Inflammation of rectum	Biopsy
Wednesday – Surgeon Mr Willis			
Jake SHAH	0900	Peptic ulcer	Vagotomy
Dipak IDOWA	1000	Haemorrhoids	Haemorrhoidectomy
Evan UPHILL	1030	Appendicitis	Appendicectomy
Brian ROBERTS	1130	Tumour	Pancreatectomy
Julian MILLNER	1200	Rectal bleeding	Sigmoidoscopy
Philip WALTERS	1230	Bloodstained vomit	Barium x-ray
Thursday – Surgeon Mr Senior			
Andrew DAVIS	0900	Diverticular disease	Colectomy
James GOODWIN	1000	Narrow pylorus	Pyloromyotomy
Henry LAMBOURN	0930	Inflammation of rectum	Biopsy
Daniel SHUKLA	1100	Giardiasis infection	Jejunal biopsy
Sydney HOBBS	1030	Abdominal pain	Barium x-ray

Move this sentence so that it becomes above NAME OF PATIENT

Some operations will have to be cancelled if an emergency operation is required.

Please sort into exact numerical order by TIME OF OPERATION within each section

Please modify layout so that OPERATION/TREATMENT column appears to the left of REASON column

Exam Practice 3 Document 4

Please key in the following document and insert the phrases as indicated. Save as GASTRO9 and print.

Insert Phrase 3 stored as GASTRO5

Dear Dr Broadstone

Re   Mr Albert Henry Smith   DoB   3/09/1928
     44 Flatwood Way   Dulcote   WELLS   BA5 9JR

The above-named attended my clinic today following a burning pain in his abdomen, particularly when his stomach was empty. He was often woken in the night by the gnawing pain. The symptoms would suggest a peptic ulcer.

An endoscopy was taken which showed a raw area in the oesophagus about 15mm across. This will most likely have been caused by regurgitation of acidic juice from the stomach.

I have prescribed a course of Aluminium Hydroxide tablets to neutralize the acid in the stomach. Self-help methods were discussed such as avoiding smoking (he has recently stopped smoking cigarettes) and drinking alcohol, coffee and tea. He was advised to eat several small meals a day.

An appointment has been made for me to see him again in 6 weeks time when a further endoscopy will be taken. If the ulcer has not healed, I would suggest we try another ulcer-healing drug, Cimeticline or Ranitidine.

Insert Phrase 2 stored as GASTRO4

Top plus 2 please. One file copy and one for Appointments Clerk. Indicate routing.

Exam Practice 4 Document 1

> Please recall this document stored under DERMA1 and amend as shown. Change to double-linespacing, except where indicated, and use a justified right margin. Adjust the line length to either (a) 12.5 cm or (b) 50 characters. If proportional spacing is used, please adjust line length to (a). Save as DERMA6 and print one copy.

> Change the word roots to follicles throughout this document.

> Men normally have thicker skin than women, but it usually becomes thinner in both with age.

> Copy this paragraph (A) to B

DERMATOLOGY

THE SKIN AND SOME DISORDERS

> acts as a barrier shielding

The skin's main function is a protective one. ~~It is vulnerable to minor injury.~~ It ~~shields~~ the internal organs of the body from injury, harmful sunlight and bacteria. It is the body's largest organ and through wear and tear cells are continually being replaced.

Skin forms the outermost covering of the body tissue. It varies in thickness from 0.05 mm to 5 mm with the thinnest skin being found on the eyelid to the thickest on the sole of the foot or palm of the hand.

The structure of skin consists of an outer layer of cells, the epidermis, a thicker inner layer, the dermis, and a deeper subcutaneous layer which contains fat.

Hair and nails are extensions of the skin. They are composed mainly of keratin, which is one of a family of proteins that also make up a major constituent of the outer layer of the epidermis. Most of the cells in the epidermis are specialised to produce keratin and some of the cells produce melanin. > which gives skin colour. Melanocytes cells are at the base of the hair roots. The dermis contains > most of the living elements blood vessels, lymph vessels and nerves. In the deeper parts of the dermis are hair roots, sweat glands and sebaceous glands. The sebaceous glands ~~produce~~ > provide a protective, oily substance called sebum. This provides a thin film of fat over the skin and nourishes the hair roots.

The epidermis is water proof and the outermost part of the epidermis has a protective coating and water-holding capacity. This all helps to maintain the body balance of fluid and electrolytes. Skin becomes cracked if the water level drops below a certain level.

Main symptoms of skin disorder are:

> The name subcutaneous ~~being~~ is derived from the anatomical name for skin – cutis

rash
lumps
itching
skin abnormalities

Skin disorders are seldom life-threatening, but they can cause distress to the sufferer often leading to psychological problems.

Move this paragraph to (B)

Diagnosis of most skin disorders can be taken from the physical characteristic of the disorder. Diagnosis by the removal of skin tissue for microscopic analysis (skin biopsy) is usually taken to exclude skin cancer problems.

The most common viral infections

~~Viral infections and inflammation~~ of the skin are cold sores and warts. Bacterial infections include boils and impetigo, whilst common fungal infections include athlete's foot and tinea (ringworm).

This paragraph only in single line spacing

~~Certain skin diseases are hereditary.~~ *Some forms of eczema, which is an itchy skin condition, affects young children, particularly those with a family history of allergic type illnesses such as asthma.*

(B)

(A)

Inset CUTIS to appear as a header on every page.

Exam Practice 4 Document 2

Recall this document stored as DERMA 2
Amend as shown. Save as DERMA 7 and
print one copy.

Atopic Eczema — Emphasise this heading

Eczema is an inflammation of the skin, causing itching and red scaly skin. Atopic eczema is common in babies and young children. It affects approximately one in 8 babies. Although there is no permanent cure, about 50 per cent of children grow out of it by the age of 6, and most children have outgrown it by puberty. (leave a space of at least 50mm here) Some practical guidelines to ease and control the problem include:

2   cutting finger nails short
6   keeping away from household pets
1   dressing in loose cotton clothing
4   swimming in the sea
3   avoiding biological washing powders
5   limiting intake of milk, eggs and cheese

Sort into exact numerical order and inset 25mm from the left margin

It usually starts with an intensely itchy rash on the face, behind the ears, in the inner creases of the elbow or behind the knees.

Small red pimples appear on the scaling skin and as the child scratches the pimples they ooze and form crusts.

Atopic eczema is not infectious. It cannot be passed from one person to another.

Centre this section

Exam Practice 4 Document 3

> Key in the following table. Save as DERMA8
> and print one copy. Do not rule the table.

THE LIBERTY HEALTH CENTRE

The following table is a typical dermatology survey taken over the last 3 months.

PATIENT NAME	AGE	DIAGNOSIS AND TREATMENT	
		TREATMENT/ MEDICATION	DISORDER

Inflammation disorders

CAMBELL Nina	1	Emollient cream	Atopic eczema
PADGET Susan	49	Corticosteroid ointment	Statis eczema
BROOKS Elaine	37	Corticosteroid ointment	Contact dermatitis
POTTINGER Audrey	18	Phototherapy	Digoid psoriasis
WRAY Edwin	21	Dithranol ointment	Discoid psoriasis
WILSON Jeremy	5	Emollient cream	Atopic eczema

Infection disorders

COTTON Ian	51	Antifungal cream	Athlete's foot
ARMSTRONG Anne	8	Salicylic acid plasters	Plantar wart
MURPHY Belinda	29	Acyclovir tablets	Herpes simplex
STENNER May	15	Griseofulvin tablets	Tinea pedis
VINCENT Adrienne	40	Antifungal powder	Athlete's foot

Other disorders

DARMANIN Mohammed	30	Corticosteroid injection	Keloid
DIXON Mandy	7	Antihistamine cream	Horsefly bite
GREENWOOD Roy	11	Antitetanus injection	Dog bite
HILL Duncan	14	Antibiotic lotion	Acne vulgaris
McKENZIE Joy	83	Wet dressing	Venous ulcer

> Please modify layout so that Infection disorders
> come before Inflammation disorders

> Please sort into exact alphabetical order by PATIENT NAME within each section

> Please modify layout so that DISORDER column appears to the left of TREATMENT/MEDICATION column

Please key in the following document and insert the phrases as indicated. Save as DERMA9 and print

Insert Phrase 3 stored as DERMA5

Dear Dr Khan

Re Richard John Manning   DOB 6/2/39
4 Parson's Way Wookey Hole   WELLS BA5 4UJ

I saw this 59 year old man at my clinic yesterday. He has suffered from irritation and redness of the skin in both sides of the groin for the past ten months. From our discussion I understand he was firstly prescribed an antifungal cream to be applied twice daily. The active ingredient in the cream was ~~miconazole~~ miconazole designed to destroy the fungus and its spores. After treatment the symptoms had not improved.

He was then diagnosed as having psoriasis, and was prescribed a 'ready diluted' topical steroid cream with the active ingredient betamethasone and chlorocresol preservative to reduce the redness and itchiness. He was aware of the danger of over using this cream as it could thin the skin.

Insert Phrase 1 stored as DERMA3

I have prescribed one of the high strength topical steroid creams which is a strong and rapidly effective treatment.

I have arranged to see him again in 2 months time. If there is no improvement, I will arrange for him to have Psoralens and ultraviolet A treatment.

Yours sincerely

Miss Christine Tsang
Dermatologist

Top plus 2 please
One for Physiotherapy
Department and one for
file. Indicate routing

Exam Practice 5 Document 1

[Handwritten instruction box:] Please recall this document stored under NEURO1 and amend as shown. Change to double-linespacing, except where indicated, and use a justified right margin. Adjust the line length to either (a) 12.5cm or (b) 50 characters. If proportional spacing is used, please adjust line length to (a). Save as NEURO6 and print one copy.

[Handwritten instruction box:] Insert THE NERVOUS SYSTEM to appear as a header on every page

[Handwritten instruction box:] Change the word tremble to tremor throughout this document

NEUROLOGY AND NEUROSURGERY

[Margin annotation: Copy this paragraph to (A)]

Neurology is the study of the nervous system, its diseases and malfunction. The nervous system is divided into two main areas; the central nervous system and the autonomic nervous system. The central nervous system comprises the brain *[insert: brain stem]* and the spinal cord, which consists of billions of interconnecting nerve cells (neurons).

[B] *[insert: Sensory nerves pass signals]* ~~Sense organs pass input~~ to the central nervous system. These include physical feeling such as pain, touch, heat and cold. The motor nerves instruct the body to react in certain ways. For example, the sweat glands work when it is hot.

[Margin annotation: Move this paragraph to (B)]

The main function of the nervous system is to gather information ~~about~~ *[insert: and interpret changes in]* conditions inside and outside the body. ~~The central nervous system analyses this information~~. The most powerful drive we have is for survival. The nervous system initiates unconsciously the drive to avoid physical pain and it responds to cold by shivering.

[✓] The autonomic part of the nervous system consists of two particular groups of nerves - the sympathetic and the parasympathetic. The primary concern of the sympathetic system is to ~~prepare~~ *[act]* the body for action. It stimulates functions such as heart rate, blood pressure and the circulation of blood to the limbs. The parasympathetic system has the opposite effect, it slows down the heart rate.

The two systems act in conjunction and so maintain the fine *[insert: adjustment]* balance needed. During times of exercise the sympathetic is the predominating system, whilst the parasympathetic system has more control during sleep.

[A] Neurosurgery is concerned with the surgical treatment of disorders of the brain, spinal cord and other parts of the nervous system. These disorders include tumours and abnormalities of the blood vessels that supply the brain. Some birth defects such as spina bifida and hydrocephalus are other disorders. Brain abscesses and intracerebral haemorrhage, certain types of epilepsy and nerve damage caused by accidents or illness are all disorders that are treated by neurosurgeons. Some of the main symptoms of a nervous disorder are:

[Margin annotation: This paragraph only in single linespacing]

[Handwritten insert box:] It also stimulates secretion of adrenaline and noradrenaline into the blood stream.

[Handwritten insert box:] These are called aneurysms, being an abnormal swelling at a weak point of an artery.

convulsion

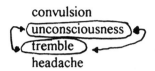

headache

Parkinson's disease is a neurological disorder that causes muscle tremble, stiffness and weakness. A slight tremble in one hand is usually the first sign of the disease. It is caused by either degeneration of or damage to nerve cells in the basal ganglia in the brain. The basal ganglia (paired nerve cell clusters) play a very important part in producing smooth muscular actions.

In the United Kingdom there are about 1500 new cases of Parkinson's disease [mainly in the elderly [each year. There is no cure for this disease. Treatment can include drugs, exercise and special aids in the home.

~~Levodopa is usually the most efficient drug.~~

Exam Practice 5 Document 2

> Recall this document stored as NEURO2. Amend as shown. Save as NEURO7 and print one copy.

QUANTOCK DISTRICT HOSPITAL

CONFERENCE ON PARKINSON'S DISEASE AND PARKINSONISM

Our hospital is to host the above one day conference next year. Arrangements for this are proceeding and the following is a draft of the topics to be covered.

1 General introduction
4 Update on the use of physiotherapy
3 Dietary aspects of management
5 Neurophysiology of swallowing
2 Concepts of managing a chronic disease
7 The way forward
6 Specialist nurses impact

> Sort into exact numerical order and inset 25mm from the left margin

> Leave at least 50mm here

The aim of the conference is to focus on the science and practice of multidisciplinary care in Parkinson's disease. The above programme covers:

FORMAT   Lectures, discussions, videos and
                  demonstrations

COST   To be finalised but approximately
                  £105 plus VAT inclusive of lunch
                  and refreshments

AIMED AT   Primary carers, General Practitioners,
                  Specialist nurses, geriatricians, neurologists
                  and nursing home staff.

As our population ages, Parkinson's disease becomes more and more prevalent. About one in every 200 people has the disease and it is more common in men than women.

A complete programme with application form will be mailed to all interested parties nearer the time.

> Emphasise and centre this section

Exam Practice 5 Document 3

Key in the following table. Same as NEURO 8 and print one copy. Do not rule the table.

QUANTOCK DISTRICT HOSPICE

Check the name here from Document 2 and amend if necessary

The following staff development courses will be available this year.

COURSE DESCRIPTION	NUMBER OF DAYS	GENERAL INFORMATION	
		VENUE	COURSE FEE
Courses January - April			
Counselling skills	2	Plymouth	£110.00
Complementary therapies	1	Fareham	£55.00
Drugs and the elderly	1	Leicester	£42.55
Leg ulcer care	1	Swindon	£47.55
Physical fitness	2	Woking	£95.50
Courses September - December			
Acupuncture	3	London	£304.00
Children with epilepsy	2	Cardiff	£140.00
Contraception: hormonal update	1	Southampton	£85.00
Evidence-based child health	3	Guildford	£300.00
Haematology/Oncology update	1	Bath	£25.00
Courses May - August			
Antiseptics in infection control	1	Harrow	£105.00
Endoscopy update	1	Brighton	£73.50
Massage and aromatherapy	1	Manchester	£44.95
Innovations in cardiac care	2	London	£100.00
Wound care	1	Swansea	£55.50
Neurosciences	1	Oxford	£60.00

Please modify layout so that September - December courses follow May - August courses

Please sort into exact alphabetical order by COURSE DESCRIPTION within each section

Please modify layout so that COURSE FEE column appears to the left of VENUE column

Exam Practice 5 Document 4

Please key in the following document and insert the phrases as indicated. Save as NEURO9 and print.

Insert Phrase 3 stored as NEURO5

Dear Dr Khan

Re   Tiffanie Emma Croft   DOB   14/04/91

19 Hill View   Woodbury   WELLS   BA5 1HP

Thank you for referring the above-named child to me. Her mother has explained in full detail how Tiffanie fell in the school dining hall and cut her left wrist on some broken glass from the tumbler which she dropped. This resulted in a deep tear in her wrist over the flexor muscle, very close to the ulnar artery. Tiffanie was treated by you that afternoon when, under a local anaesthetic, you closed the wound by means of mattress sutures.

After a few days Tiffanie complained of blood seeping from the wound and pins and needles in her left arm and hand. You suspected some damage to the ulnar nerve and tendon and referred her to me.

I have thoroughly examined the wound today and have made arrangements for Tiffanie to be admitted as soon as possible. Under a general anaesthetic I will repair the damage to both the ulnar nerve and the tendon.

Insert Phrase 2 stored as NEURO4

Top plus 2 please. One file copy and one for PAEDIATRIC WARD. Indicate routing.

Proofreading Exercise 1

2 The most commonly effected veins are the saphenous (superficial) veins of the legs. There is an inherited tendency to varicose veins, but obstruction to blood flow is responsible in some cases. Complications can occur such as thrombosis phlebitis and
3 haemorhage. Treatment includes elastic support, stripping or in some cases excision .

4 there are various grades of elastic support available, from those designed for early
5 varicose veins through to those for pa6ients with really severe problems. The elastic support is designed to improve circulation, ease the discomfort or pain and in severe cases conceal blemishes. Supports come in different hosiery styles and include thigh,
6 open toad thigh, below knee and open toe below knee. There are also support hose
7 8 available formen which are indistinguishable from normal socks,

Errors

1 Headings should always be emphasised
2 Keying error – **effected** for **affected**
3 Failure to key in double letter – **haemorhage** for **haemorrhage**
4 Capital letter required at start of sentence
5 Inaccurate fingering – **pa6ients** for **patients**
6 Incorrect spelling of **toed**
7 Space missing between **for** and **men**
8 Full stop needed at end of sentence

Proofreading Exercise 2

REGAINING CONTROL OF YOUR BLADDER

1 2 In britain today there are about 3 million poeple of all ages who have lost some control over when and where they pass urine. This condition is known as incontinence. There are two types of incontinence, stress and urge.

3 4 If your leakage from the blasser occurs when sneezing. coughing or exercising, this is stress incontinence. The leakage, which may even occur when walking, is caused by a
5 weakening of the bladder out let and pelvic floor muscles. It can affect women of all ages.

6 patients who suffer a sudden need to pass urine but are unable to reach the toilet in time
7 are suffering from urge incontinence. They may also need to pass u8rine more often than
8 usual and may have to get up several times in the night. Bed-wetting is also a symptum. This condition is often caused by an overactive or unstable bladder, and tends to happen as people get older. There is often less warning and the bladder needs emptying more often.

An overactive bladder may be trained at home by suppressing the contractions. This is done by gradually increasing the capacity of the bladder and the time interval between passing water. If a patient experiences difficulty when trying to do this, they may find the following suggestions helpful:

1 make a drink
9 2   sit on the feet
3 cross the legs
4 sit on a rolled up towel

10 It is important for patients to keep up fluid intake of 8-12 cups a day, andto continue with pelvic floor exercises.

Errors

1 Capital letter needed for place name
2 Transposition of letters in **people**
3 Incorrect keying in – **blasser** for **bladder**
4 Full stop used instead of comma between items
5 **Outlet** should be one word

6   Capital letter needed at the start of a sentence
7   Inaccurate fingering – **u8rine** for **urine**
8   Incorrect spelling of **symptom**
9   Item 2 misaligned
10   Space missing between **and** and **to**

Proofreading Exercise 3

Registration No: R 9701969

date of keying-in

1   Mrs Edwina Barber
          57 White Horse Road
2   Westbury
    Wilts
    BA12 8LE

Dear Mrs Barber

The following appointment has been made for you to see

MR L JUCK, CONSULTANT OPHTHALMOLOGIST
at WARMINSTER HOSPITAL

Appointment: (insert date for second Thursday, 2-months time) at 10.15 am

3   On arrival please report to the Reception Disk which is at the main entrance and you
    will be directed to the out-patient waiting area,

4   transport has not been arranged for this appointment unless otherwise stated. should
5   you require transport it is neceSsary for you to contact your GP who will arrange this
    for you.

6   Please bring detials of your current medication.

7 8 IT IS ADVICED BY THE CONSULTENT THAT YOU DO NOT DRIVE
    YOURSELF TO THE CLINIC, AS IT MAY BE NECESSARY TO PUT DROPS
    INTO YOUR EYES WHICH MAY BLUR YOUR VISION.

    IF YOU CANNOT KEEP THIS APPOINTMENT IT IS IMPORTANT THAT YOU
9   PHONE MR LUCK'S SECRETARY ON 01985 123456 AS SOON AS POSSIBLE,
10 SO THAT THIS APOINTMENT CAN BE OFFERED TO ANOTHER PATIENT.

Yours sincerely

E M MEDLAR (Mrs)
MEDICAL SECRETARY

Errors

1   Address misaligned
2   Postal town should always be in closed capitals
3   Spelling error – **Disk** for **Desk**
4   Capital letter needed at the start of a sentence
5   Keying error – **neceSsary** for **necessary**
6   Letters transposed – **detials** for **details**
7   Keying or spelling error – **ADVICED** for **ADVISED**
8   Keying or spelling error – **CONSULTENT** for **CONSULTANT**
9   Spelling error – **LUCK'S** for **JUCK'S**
10   Failure to key in double letter – **APOINTMENT** for **APPOINTMENT**

Exam Practice 1 Document 1

NATURAL CURES AND THE METABOLISM

HERBAL MEDICINE

From the earliest of times, herbs have been used for their healing abilities and for pain relief. We still rely on the curative properties of plants in about 75 per cent of our medicines today.

Throughout the world, thousands of plant species have medicinal uses. They contain active constituents that have a direct action on the metabolism. These constituents are used in both herbal and conventional medicines offering benefits that pharmaceutical drugs often lack. Herbal medicine often complements conventional treatments. They can provide safe remedies for chronic illnesses.

Most commonly used herbs are extremely safe to use. A few plants can have side-effects for some people. Like all medicines, herbal remedies must be treated with respect. A well-trained practitioner will be able to help and give guidance. Dosages must be carefully followed.

Ephedra is an evergreen shrub with long, narrow stems and tiny leaves. It is used principally as a treatment for asthma, hay fever and for the acute onset of colds and influenza. It can help to raise blood pressure, cool fever and alleviate rheumatism. Whilst it can help all these ailments, it can also be extremely toxic when taken at the wrong dosage.

Depending on the chemical constituents that a herbal medicine contains, the metabolism is affected in different ways. Research is still being

Exam Practice 1 Document 1 continued

NATURAL CURES AND THE METABOLISM

undertaken into plant constituents. Plants contain hundreds of different constituents that interact in complex ways.

Good health depends on having a balanced nervous system. Long term good health of the nervous system requires one to look at the demands of life. Excessive anxiety, worry or depression should be avoided.

The nervous system is linked with the endocrine system which controls the release of hormones. It is also linked with the immune system. This system controls the resistance to infection and recovery from illness and injury. This complex of systems, part electrical, part chemical and part mechanical must function in harmony if good health is to be maintained.

Many herbs work with the immune, nervous and endocrine systems and they are effective because they work in line with the body's processes. Ginseng has oval, toothed leaves and clusters of green-yellow flowers. This herb is an adaptogenic, it can help people to adapt, by supporting the nervous system. It can be an effective remedy at times of great mental or physical stress. It also can be taken when a relaxing effect is required, for example to get a good night's rest, or to relieve a headache.

A way of classifying medicinal plants is to identify their action - whether they are antiseptic, sedative, or diuretic and the way they affect the metabolism differently.

2

Exam Practice 1 Document 2

The Medicinal Herb Garden

When planning a herb garden take into account the amount of space available, soil conditions and climate. Choose a range of hardy herbs that will establish themselves quickly and produce an abundance of foliage that can be harvested.

The following plants should grow well:

Fever few
Lemon balm
Marigold
Peppermint
Rosemary
Sage
St John's wort
Thyme

Some medicinal plants can be grown in

pots
containers
window boxes

or even hanging baskets. Bay laurel is an ideal plant for growing in a container but care must be taken to prevent it from drying out or becoming pot-bound.

There is a wide variety of propagation methods including seeds, cuttings, root division and layering. Taking cuttings is the most popular method. Cuttings are usually taken from the stem but some may be taken from the roots. Do not feed or mulch medicinal herbs as this reduces their therapeutic strength.

Cultivated herb gardens create an aromatic, colourful area providing fresh herbs to use medicinally and in cooking.

Exam Practice 1 Document 1 continued

NATURAL CURES AND THE METABOLISM

From the earliest of times, herbs have been used for their healing abilities and for pain relief. We still rely on the curative properties of plants in about 75 per cent of our medicines today.

3

Exam Practice 1 Document 4

Quantock District Hospital

County Bridge Road
TAUNTON
TA1 7AB
01749 123456

Herbal/Homeopathy Clinic
Himiyah Kasan MNIMH
Medical Herbalist

HK/your initials/MH47229

Dr A J Wright
The Liberty Health Centre
The Liberty
WELLS
BA5 2FX

Date of typing

Dear Dr Wright

Re Ms Lavinia Rushton DOB 19/12/75
Mendip Cottage, Coxley WELLS BA5 7WP

This lady was seen today at the above clinic. As you know she would like to become pregnant by her partner but she is having difficulty in conceiving.

As this was her first visit we discussed her family traits, diet, lifestyle and any anxieties or stress she may have. I gave her a physical examination. I have also sent her urine for analysis and a blood test was taken to measure her haemoglobin level.

Her menstrual cycle is regular and she stopped taking the progestogen-only oral contraceptive pill six months ago. She is not overweight and she exercises regularly, mainly by having a brisk walk whilst out with her dogs.

On her work situation she has a small amount of stress, but this together with her failing to conceive is building up her stress and anxiety levels. We discussed the importance of a well-balanced diet, exercise and time for relaxation. I have suggested she would benefit from attending the Yoga exercise classes organised by the Cardiology Department.

I have prescribed her a course of agnus castus tablets as these will help her low progesterone level, and have made an appointment to see her again in 6 weeks' time.

Yours sincerely

Himiyah Kasan
Medical Herbalist

cc Dr Jordanna Cutajar
   File

cc Dr Jordanna Cutajar
   File

Exam Practice 1 Document 3

QUANTOCK DISTRICT HOSPITAL

HERBAL/HOMEOPATHIC DEPARTMENT

Listed below are the stock numbers of herbal treatments we keep for use with the more common ailments we come across at our monthly clinic.

COMMON AILMENT	STOCK NUMBER	GENERAL REMEDIES	
		REMEDY	HERB USED
Digestive disorders			
Stomach spasm	52	Flowerhead infusion	Chamomile
Acidity and indigestion	54	Bark infusion	Slippery elm
Diarrhoea	55	Decoction of herb	Agrimony
Constipation	57	Root decoction	Yellow dock
Mouth and tongue ulcers	58	Tincture or powder	Myrrh resin
Nerve and stress related problems			
Migraine headache	45	50ml infusion	Rosemary leaves
Neuralgia	47	Infused oil	St John's wort
Sinus headache	48	Tea bag infusion	Lime flowers
Toothache	51	Chew a clove	Dried clove
Insomnia	52	Tincture with water	Hops
Reproductive, pregnancy and menstrual problems			
Pre-menstrual tension	81	Tablets or tincture	Valerian
Fluid retention	84	Leaf infusion	Dandelion
Nausea and sickness	85	Seed infusion	Fennel
Fertility problems (women)	92	Tablets or tincture	Agnus castus
Haemorrhoids	96	Ointment	Witch hazel bark
Decreased oestrogen	97	Tablets	Helonias root

GROWTH CYCLE

The enlarging uterus can easily be felt at 16 weeks. Some women may have a warm, flushed feeling. They may have an increased appetite together with a gain in weight. Feelings of nausea and frequency to pass urine usually cease between 13 to 28 weeks, and the woman may feel generally better, with more energy than she did in the earlier weeks.

At this time a woman's heart rate and volume of blood pumped to the heart increases. This can put a strain on the heart of women with existing heart disorders. This is to allow the fetus to develop properly.

For some women stretch-marks develop on the abdomen, breasts and thighs during the final weeks. In a first pregnancy the baby's head drops down low into the pelvis at about week 36. In subsequent pregnancies this is usually later.

Some minor problems that can occur during pregnancy are haemorrhoids, constipation, heartburn and a craving to eat substances such as clay or coal. Varicose veins, swollen ankles, leg cramps and headaches are also common during late pregnancy.

The average weight increase in pregnancy is 12.7 kg. Seventy per cent of this occurs during the last 20 weeks. At full term a typical fetus would weigh 3.4 kg, the placenta and fluid together 1.4 kg, leaving the rest of the weight to be water retention.

2

Exam Practice 2 Document 1

GROWTH CYCLE

OBSTETRICS

SOME FACTS ABOUT PREGNANCY

During pregnancy a single microscopic cell develops into a fully grown baby containing in excess of 6 million cells. A human being grows more rapidly in the womb than at any other time.

The first most obvious sign of pregnancy is a lack of menstrual bleeding. Changes in the body start by the breasts beginning to swell and becoming tender as the mammary glands develop. There is an urge to pass urine more frequently and often a white discharge from the vagina. Nausea and vomiting, particularly in the morning, are very common symptoms.

A typical pregnancy lasts from 38 to 40 weeks and this is counted from the first day of the last menstrual bleeding. This period of time can be broken into three parts - 0 to 12 weeks, 13 to 28 weeks and 29 to 40 weeks. For the first 8 weeks the developing baby is called an embryo and after that time a fetus.

In the first 4 weeks since conception the egg develops to approximately 3 mm in length. After 6 weeks it grows to approximately 25 mm and the embryo inside it measures almost 10 mm long. By 8 weeks the embryo has most of its organs. It is during the first 12 weeks of pregnancy that the growing baby is most vulnerable to damage.

Exam Practice 2 Document 2

THE LIBERTY HEALTH CENTRE

Antenatal Clinic

Our clinics are held each week on a Tuesday and Thursday morning. After your initial visit, you should attend once a month until the 28th week, every two weeks until the 36th week and then weekly until the 40th week (your delivery date).

Your first visit to the clinic is the most thorough and the longest. A midwife will take a small sample of blood to be examined for anaemia and folic acid deficiency and to check your blood group. A urine test for proteinuria will also be taken and your blood pressure will be checked for hypertension.

You will be invited to attend childbirth preparation classes, when information is given on the following

   1 what happens during labour
   2 advice on exercise and diet
   3 breathing exercises
   4 pain relief available
   5 relaxation techniques
   6 postnatal period

An insight will be given concerning postnatal care. Temperature, blood pressure and pulse will be monitored regularly. Instruction on pelvic floor exercises to restore muscle tone will also be given.

Exam Practice 2 Document 1 continued

GROWTH CYCLE

During pregnancy a single microscopic cell develops into a fully grown baby containing in excess of 6 million cells. A human being grows more rapidly in the womb than at any other time.

3

Exam Practice 2 Document 4

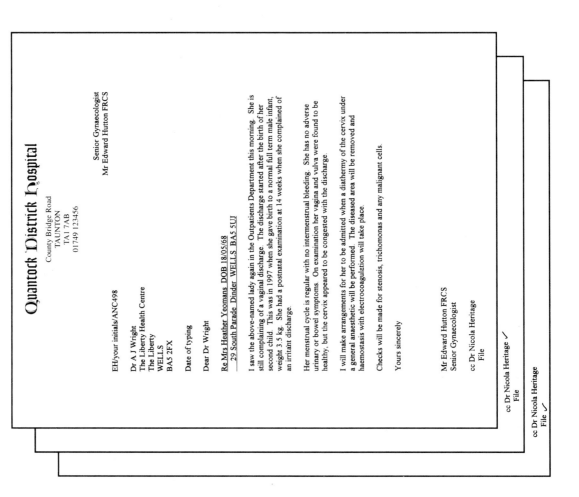

Quantock District Hospital

County Bridge Road
TAUNTON
TA1 7AB
01749 123456

Senior Gynaecologist
Mr Edward Hutton FRCS

EH/your initials/ANC498

Dr A J Wright
The Liberty Health Centre
The Liberty
WELLS
BA5 2FX

Date of typing

Dear Dr Wright

Re Mrs Heather Yeomans DOB 18/05/68
29 South Parade Dinder WELLS BA5 5UJ

I saw the above-named lady again in the Outpatients Department this morning. She is still complaining of a vaginal discharge. The discharge started after the birth of her second child. This was in 1997 when she gave birth to a normal full term male infant, weight 3.5 kg. She had a postnatal examination at 14 weeks when she complained of an irritant discharge.

Her menstrual cycle is regular with no intermenstrual bleeding. She has no adverse urinary or bowel symptoms. On examination her vagina and vulva were found to be healthy, but the cervix appeared to be congested with the discharge.

I will make arrangements for her to be admitted when a diathermy of the cervix under a general anaesthetic will be performed. The diseased area will be removed and haemostasis with electrocoagulation will take place.

Checks will be made for stenosis, trichomonas and any malignant cells.

Yours sincerely

Mr Edward Hutton FRCS
Senior Gynaecologist

cc Dr Nicola Heritage
   File

cc Dr Nicola Heritage ✓
   File

cc Dr Nicola Heritage ✓
   File

Exam Practice 2 Document 3

THE LIBERTY HEALTH CENTRE

Antenatal clinic details for patients who may have some problems throughout their pregnancy.

After their consultation here, these patients will need to be referred to Dr Nicola Heritage

PATIENT'S NAME	DAY	TIME OF APPOINTMENT	GENERAL DESCRIPTION PROCEDURE/ CONCERN
First visit to clinic			
DAVIES Melanie	Tuesday	0900	Cervical smear, no recent test
HALIDAY Gemma	Thursday	1100	Blood test for anaemia
HARRISON Hayley	Thursday	1130	Urine test for proteinuria
HOUSTON Greta	Tuesday	0930	Blood test for hepatitis B
SIMPSON Diana	Tuesday	1000	Blood test to check group
12 week visit to clinic			
CROSS Suk Kam	Thursday	0900	Raised blood pressure
FLYNN Paula	Tuesday	1030	Blood test for Rubella
GRAY Kirsty	Thursday	0930	Severe vomiting
HENVILLE Jodie	Tuesday	1000	Swollen ankles
HODGE Erica	Thursday	1000	Raised blood pressure
WILLIAMS Helen	Tuesday	1100	Unexplained weight gain
16-18 week visit to clinic			
BUCKLE Marcia	Thursday	1030	Amniocentesis for spina bifida
KNOX Jessica	Thursday	1100	Fetoscopy for fetal disorder
LAMB Amy	Tuesday	1030	Amniocentesis for spina bifida
ROBERTS Dalta	Tuesday	1100	Blood test for anaemia
STONE Carol	Thursday	1130	Fetoscopy for fetal disorder

2

and pepsin from the stomach lining helps to break down proteins in the food. The continual churning action of the stomach mechanically turns the food into a semi-fluid mass called chyme. This is then released into the duodenum.

Whilst passing through the duodenum, the food is broken down further by bile salts and acids produced by the liver and released from the gall bladder and enzymes from the pancreas. These enzymes further break down carbohydrates, protein and fats.

The duodenum leads into the small intestine and here, additional enzymes produced by glands in the lining complete the final breakdown of the food. Nutrients are absorbed by the thin lining of the intestine into the bloodstream and lymphatic system.

The final stage is for the food residue to pass through the large intestine, where much of the water is absorbed through the lining of the colon. Undigested and dehydrated residue then passes into the rectum and anus ready to be expelled.

Food spends the following approximate time going through the digestive system. One minute in the mouth breaking the food down followed by 10 seconds in the oesophagus. It is in the stomach between 2 and 4 hours and the small intestine for 1 to 6 hours. It can be in the large intestine from 10 hours up to several days.

The Digestive System

GASTROENTEROLOGY

Gastroenterology is the study of the digestive system and a specialist in this branch of medicine is called a gastroenterologist. He or she treats patients by advising on diet and lifestyle, prescribing medication when necessary and referring patients for surgical treatment, for example appendicectomy.

The digestive system is the group of organs consisting of the alimentary canal which forms a continuous passage from the mouth to the anus, and various other associated organs. This group of organs breaks down food into the various chemical components that the body can absorb and use for energy. These components, carbohydrates, sugar, fats, proteins, minerals and vitamins, are also used to build and repair body cells and tissues.

Digestion starts when food enters the mouth. It is broken down and chewed by the teeth and then the salivary glands secrete saliva to lubricate it. The saliva also contains enzymes that break down the carbohydrates. The tongue (which contains taste buds) manipulates the food into small balls, called bolus ready for easy swallowing.

From the mouth the food passes without changing, through the pharynx, and into the oesophagus. Peristalsis, waves of muscular contractions, carries the food down the oesophagus to the stomach. Hydrochloric acid

The Digestive System

Exam Practice 3 Document 1

3

The digestive tract is very tolerant of what is passed through it but it reacts strongly against infected foods, poisons and other irritants causing vomiting or diaorrhea. Indigestion is a very common disorder.

Gastroenterology is the study of the digestive system and a specialist in this branch of medicine is called a gastroenterologist. He or she treats patients by advising on diet and lifestyle, prescribing medication when necessary and referring patients for surgical treatment, for example appendicectomy.

The Digestive System

Exam Practice 3 Document 2

QUANTOCK DISTRICT HOSPITAL

Recruitment drive for Staff Nurses Grade E in the Gastroenterology Wards.

The following is a summary of what will be on the information sheet we send out to prospective applicants:

caring and dedicated staff
friendly and dynamic team
in-house learning opportunities
job satisfaction
paid study leave
promotional opportunities

In addition to the above there will be information on:

TRAINING	Travel scholarship ENB998 and A24 funding
AMENITIES	Subsidised canteen Hospital accommodation Licensed social club Tennis courts
SALARY	£14,191 - £16,440 working 37½ hours per week

We also have an on-site nursery, a counselling service and fully equipped library.

The use of endoscopes has meant that many major operations are now only minor ones. The gastroscope is a flexible fibre-optic endoscope and is used to check disorders of the oesophagus, stomach and duodenum.

Experience of assisting with the work involving endoscopes is necessary for this post. The position will also involve the care of patients and their relatives from admission to discharge.

For further information please contact:

Mrs Amara Aluko
Quantock District Hospital
County Bridge Road
TAUNTON
TA1 7AB

Quantock District Hospital

County Bridge Road
TAUNTON
TA1 7AB
01749 123456

Consultant Gastroenterologist
Mr G W Martin MRCS

GWM/your initials/47549

Dr W Broadstone
The Liberty Health Centre
The Liberty
WELLS
BA5 2FX

Date of typing

Dear Dr Broadstone

Re Mr Albert Henry Smith DOB 3/09/1928
47 Flatwood Way Dulcote WELLS BA5 9JR

The above-named attended my clinic today following a burning pain in his abdomen, particularly when his stomach was empty. He was often woken in the night by the gnawing pain. These symptoms would suggest a peptic ulcer.

An endoscopy was taken which showed a raw area in the oesophagus about 15 mm across. This will most likely have been caused by regurgitation of acidic juice from the stomach.

I have prescribed a course of Aluminium Hydroxide tablets to neutralise the acid in the stomach. Self-help methods were discussed such as avoiding smoking (he has recently stopped smoking cigarettes) and drinking alcohol, coffee and tea. He was advised to eat several small meals a day.

An appointment has been made for me to see him again in 6 weeks time when a further endoscopy will be taken. If the ulcer has not healed, I would suggest we try another ulcer-healing drug, Cimeticline or Ranitidine.

Please refer him to me without an appointment if the matter becomes urgent.

Yours sincerely

Mr G W Martin MRCS
Consultant Gastroenterologist

cc Appointments Clerk
File

cc Appointments Clerk ✓
File

cc Appointments Clerk
File ✓

QUANTOCK DISTRICT HOSPITAL

List of patients in the Gastroenterology Wards to have operations/treatment this week.

Some operations will have to be cancelled if an emergency operation is required.

NAME OF PATIENT	TIME OF OPERATION	OPERATION/ TREATMENT	DIAGNOSIS REASON

Tuesday - Surgeon Mr Senior

Michaela YEE	0900	Anal fissure	Ulcer
Sophie MADSEN	1000	Appendicectomy	Appendicitis
Carolyn WOOD	1030	Haemorrhoidectomy	Haemorrhoids
Tara HENDERSON	1100	Biopsy	Inflammation of rectum
Diane McKENZIE	1130	Pancreatectomy	Tumour

Wednesday - Surgeon Mr Willis

Jake SHAH	0900	Vagotomy	Peptic ulcer
Dipak IDOWA	1000	Haemorrhoidectomy	Haemorrhoids
Evan UPHILL	1030	Appendicectomy	Appendicitis
Brian ROBERTS	1130	Pancreatectomy	Tumour
Julian MILLER	1200	Sigmoidoscopy	Rectal bleeding
Philip WALTERS	1230	Barium x-ray	Bloodstained vomit

Thursday - Surgeon Mr Senior

Andrew DAVIS	0900	Colectomy	Diverticular disease
Henry LAMBOURN	0930	Biopsy	Inflammation of rectum
James GOODWIN	1000	Pyloromyotomy	Narrow pylorus
Sydney HOBBS	1030	Barium x-ray	Abdominal pain
Daniel SHUKLA	1100	Jejunal biopsy	Giardiasis infection

CUTIS

The dermis contains most of the living elements, blood vessels, lymph vessels and nerves. In the deeper parts of the dermis are hair follicles, sweat glands and sebaceous glands. The sebaceous glands produce a protective, oily substance called sebum. This provides a thin film of fat over the skin and nourishes the hair follicles.

The epidermis is waterproof and the outermost part of the epidermis has a protective coating and water-holding capacity. This all helps to maintain the body balance of fluid and electrolytes. Skin becomes cracked if the water level drops below a certain level.

Main symptoms of skin disorder are:

lumps

rash

itching

skin abnormalities

Skin disorders are seldom life-threatening, but they can cause distress to the sufferer often leading to psychological problems. Diagnosis of most skin disorders can be taken from the physical characteristic of the disorder. Diagnosis by the removal of skin tissue for microscopic analysis (skin biopsy) is usually taken to exclude skin cancer problems

2

CUTIS

DERMATOLOGY

THE SKIN AND SOME DISORDERS

The skin's main function is a protective one. It acts as a barrier shielding the internal organs of the body from injury, harmful sunlight and bacteria. It is the body's largest organ and cells are continually being replaced through wear and tear.

Skin forms the outermost covering of the body tissue. It varies in thickness from 0.05 mm to 5 mm with the thinnest skin being found on the eyelid to the thickest on the sole of the foot or palm of the hand. Men normally have a thicker skin than women, but it usually becomes thinner in both with age.

The structure of skin consists of an outer layer of cells, the epidermis, a thicker inner layer, the dermis, and a deeper subcutaneous layer which contains fat. The name subcutaneous is derived from the anatomical name for skin - cutis.

Hair and nails are extensions of the skin. They are composed mainly of keratin, which is one of a family of proteins that also make up a major constituent of the outer layer of the epidermis. Most of the cells in the epidermis are specialised to produce keratin and some of the cells produce melanin which gives skin colour. Melanocytes cells are at the base of the hair follicles

Exam Practice 4 Document 2

Atopic Eczema

Eczema is an inflammation of the skin, causing itching and red scaly skin. Atopic eczema is common in babies and young children. It affects approximately 1 in 8 babies. Although there is no permanent cure, about 50 per cent of children grow out of it by the age of 6, and most children have outgrown it by puberty.

Some practical guidelines to ease and control the problem include:

1. dressing in loose cotton clothing
2. cutting finger nails short
3. avoiding biological washing powders
4. swimming in the sea
5. limiting intake of milk, eggs and cheese
6. keeping away from household pets

It usually starts with an intensely itchy rash on the face, behind the ears, in the inner creases of the elbow or behind the knees.

Small red pimples appear on the scaling skin and as the child scratches the pimples they ooze and form crusts.

Atopic eczema is not infectious. It cannot be passed from one person to another.

Exam Practice 4 Document 1 continued

CUTIS

Some forms of eczema, which is an itchy skin condition, affect young children, particularly those with a family history of allergic type illnesses such as asthma.

The most common viral infections of the skin are cold sores and warts.

Bacterial infections include boils and impetigo, whilst common fungal infections include athlete's foot and tinea (ringworm).

The skin's main function is a protective one. It acts as a barrier shielding the internal organs of the body from injury, harmful sunlight and bacteria.

It is the body's largest organ and cells are continually being replaced through wear and tear.

3

Exam Practice 4 Document 4

Quantock District Hospital

County Bridge Road
TAUNTON
TA1 7AB
01749 123456

Dermatology Department
Miss Christine Tsang
Dermatologist

CT/your initials/9854239

Date of typing

Dr S Khan
The Liberty Health Centre
The Liberty
WELLS
BA5 2FX

Dear Dr Khan

Re Richard John Manning DOB 6/2/29
    4 Parson's Way Wookey Hole WELLS BA5 4UJ

I saw this 59 year old man at my clinic yesterday. He has suffered from irritation and redness of the skin in both sides of the groin for the past ten months. From our discussion I understand he was firstly prescribed an antifungal cream to be applied twice daily. The active ingredient in the cream was miconazole, designed to destroy the fungus and its spores. After treatment the symptoms had not improved.

He was then diagnosed as having psoriasis, and was prescribed a 'ready diluted' topical steroid cream with the active ingredient betamethasone and chlorocresol preservative to reduce the redness and itchiness. He was aware of the danger of over using this cream as it could thin the skin.

After a thorough examination I found no other traces of psoriasis on his body, although he did have patches of dry skin on his elbows. He has had no recent physical illness and has not been under any emotional stress.

I have prescribed one of the high strength topical steroid creams which is a strong and rapidly effective treatment.

I have arranged to see him again in 2 months time. If there is no improvement, I will arrange for him to have Psoralens and ultraviolet A treatment.

Yours sincerely

Miss Christine Tsang
Dermatologist

cc Physiotherapy Department
   File

cc Physiotherapy Department
   File

Exam Practice 4 Document 3

THE LIBERTY HEALTH CENTRE

The following table is a typical dermatology survey taken over the last 3 months.

PATIENT NAME	AGE	DISORDER	TREATMENT/ MEDICATION
Infection disorders			
ARMSTRONG Anne	8	Plantar wart	Salicylic acid plasters
COTTON Ian	51	Athlete's foot	Antifungal cream
MURPHY Belinda	29	Herpes simplex	Acyclovir tablets
STENNER May	15	Tinea pedis	Griseofulvin tablets
VINCENT Adrienne	40	Athlete's foot	Antifungal powder
Inflammation disorders			
BROOKS Elaine	37	Contact dermatitis	Corticosteroid ointment
CAMPBELL Nina	1	Atopic eczema	Emollient cream
PADGET Susan	49	Statis eczema	Corticosteroid ointment
POTTINGER Audrey	18	Discoid psoriasis	Phototherapy
WILSON Jeremy	5	Atopic eczema	Emollient cream
WRAY Edwin	21	Discoid psoriasis	Dithranol ointment
Other disorders			
DARMANIN Mohammed	30	Keloid	Corticosteroid injection
DIXON Mandy	7	Horsefly bite	Antihistamine cream
GREENWOOD Roy	11	Dog bite	Antitetanus injection
HILL Duncan	14	Acne vulgaris	Antibiotic lotion
McKENZIE Joy	83	Venous ulcer	Wet dressing

THE NERVOUS SYSTEM

conjunction and so maintain the fine adjustment balance needed. During times of exercise the sympathetic is the predominating system, whilst the parasympathetic system has more control during sleep.

Neurology is the study of the nervous system, its diseases and malfunction. The nervous system is divided into two main areas; the central nervous system and the autonomic nervous system. The central nervous system comprises the brain, brain stem and the spinal cord, which consists of billions of interconnecting nerve cells (neurons).

Neurosurgery is concerned with the surgical treatment of disorders of the brain, spinal cord and other parts of the nervous system. These disorders include tumours and abnormalities of the blood vessels that supply the brain. These are called neurysms, being an abnormal swelling at a weak point of an artery. Some birth defects such as spina bifida and hydrocephalus are other disorders. Brain abscesses and intracerebral haemorrhage, certain types of epilepsy and nerve damage caused by accidents or illness are all disorders that are treated by neurosurgeons.

Some of the main symptoms of a nervous disorder are:

convulsion

tremor

unconsciousness

headache

Parkinson's disease is a neurological disorder that causes muscle tremor, stiffness and weakness. A slight tremor in one hand is usually the first sign of the disease. It is caused by either degeneration of or damage to nerve cells in the basal ganglia in the brain. The basal ganglia (paired

2

THE NERVOUS SYSTEM

NEUROLOGY AND NEUROSURGERY

Neurology is the study of the nervous system, its diseases and malfunction. The nervous system is divided into two main areas; the central nervous system and the autonomic nervous system. The central nervous system comprises the brain, brain stem and the spinal cord, which consists of billions of interconnecting nerve cells (neurons).

The main function of the nervous system is to gather information and interpret changes in conditions inside and outside the body. The most powerful drive we have is for survival. The nervous system initiates unconsciously the drive to avoid physical pain and it responds to cold by shivering.

Sensory nerves pass signals to the central nervous system. These include physical feeling such as pain, touch, heat and cold. The motor nerves instruct the body to react in certain ways. For example, the sweat glands work when it is hot.

The autonomic part of the nervous system consists of two particular groups of nerves - the sympathetic and the parasympathetic. The primary concern of the sympathetic system is to prepare the body for action. It stimulates functions such as heart rate, blood pressure and the circulation of blood to the limbs. It also stimulates secretion of adrenaline and noradrenaline into the blood stream. The parasympathetic system has the opposite effect, it slows down the heart rate. The two systems act in

Exam Practice 5 Document 2

QUANTOCK DISTRICT HOSPITAL

CONFERENCE ON PARKINSON'S DISEASE AND PARKINSONISM

Our hospital is to host the above one day conference next year. Arrangements for this are proceeding and the following is a draft of the topics to be covered

1 General introduction
2 Concepts of managing a chronic disease
3 Dietary aspects of management
4 Update on the use of physiotherapy
5 Neurophysiology of swallowing
6 Specialist nurses impact
7 The way forward

The aim of the conference is to focus on the science and practice of multidisciplinary care in Parkinson's disease. The above programme covers:

FORMAT   Lectures, discussions, videos and demonstrations

COST   To be finalised but approximately £105 plus VAT inclusive of lunch and refreshments

AIMED AT   Primary carers, General Practitioners, specialist nurses, geriatricians, neurologists and nursing home staff

As our population ages, Parkinson's disease becomes more and more prevalent. About one in every 200 people has the disease and it is more common in men than women.

A complete programme with application form will be mailed to all interested parties nearer the time.

Exam Practice 5 Document 1 continued

THE NERVOUS SYSTEM

nerve cell clusters) play a very important part in producing smooth muscular actions.

In the United Kingdom there are about 1500 new cases of Parkinson's disease each year mainly in the elderly. There is no cure for this disease.

Treatment can include drugs, exercise and special aids in the home.

3

Quantock District Hospital

County Bridge Road
TAUNTON
TA1 7AB
01749 123456

Neurological Clinic
Mrs Helen McCallum
Consultant Neurologist

HMcC/your initials/171/4379

Dr S Khan
The Liberty Health Centre
The Liberty
WELLS
BA5 2FX

Date of typing

Dear Dr Khan

Re Tiffanie Emma Croft DOB 14/04/91
    19 Hill View Woodbury WELLS BA5 1HP

Thank you for referring the above-named child to me. Her mother has explained in full detail how Tiffanie fell in the school dining hall and cut her left wrist on some broken glass from the tumbler which she dropped. This resulted in a deep tear in her wrist over the flexor muscle, very close to the ulnar artery. Tiffanie was treated by you that afternoon when, under a local anaesthetic, you closed the wound by means of mattress sutures.

After a few days Tiffanie complained of blood seeping from the wound and pins and needles in her left arm and hand. You suspected some damage to the ulnar nerve and tendon and referred her to me.

I have thoroughly examined the wound today and have made arrangements for Tiffanie to be admitted as soon as possible. Under a general anaesthetic I will repair the damage to both the ulnar nerve and the tendon.

She has been prescribed a course of Cloxacillin, an antibacterial and antibiotic drug.

Yours sincerely

Mrs Helen McCallum
Consultant Neurologist

cc Paediatric Ward
   File

QUANTOCK DISTRICT HOSPITAL

The following staff development courses will be available this year.

GENERAL INFORMATION

COURSE DESCRIPTION	NUMBER OF DAYS	COURSE FEE	VENUE
Courses January - April			
Complementary therapies	1	£55.00	Fareham
Counselling skills	2	£110.00	Plymouth
Drugs and the elderly	1	£42.55	Leicester
Leg ulcer care	1	£47.55	Swindon
Physical fitness	2	£95.50	Woking
Courses May - August			
Antiseptics in infection control	1	£105.00	Harrow
Endoscopy update	1	£73.50	Brighton
Innovations in cardiac care	2	£100.00	London
Massage and aromatherapy	1	£74.95	Manchester
Neurosciences	1	£60.00	Oxford
Wound care	1	£55.50	Swansea
Courses September - December			
Acupuncture	3	£304.00	London
Children with epilepsy	2	£170.00	Cardiff
Contraception: hormonal update	1	£85.00	Southampton
Evidence-based child health	3	£300.00	Guildford
Haematology/Oncology update	1	£25.00	Bath

Quantock Districk Hospital

County Bridge Road
TAUNTON
TA1 7AB
01749 123456

Adenoidectomy	surgical operation to remove the adenoids
Adenoids	overgrowth of glandular tissue at the rear of the nose
Allergy (allergic)	adverse reaction of the body to a substrate
Amalgam	filling made by mixing a silver-tin alloy with mercury in a machine known as an amalgamator
Amniocentesis	a procedure used to diagnose genetic disorders in a fetus
Anaemia	a reduction of the ability of the blood to carry red blood cells
Anaesthetics	the loss of feeling
Anaphylactic shock	major allergic reaction within the body which may lead to a person's collapse
Angina	sense of suffocation or tightness in the centre of the chest, often accompanied by pain
Anti-inflammatory	drug that reduces inflammation
Antibiotic	a medicine derived from living organisms, usually bacteria or moulds, that kills microorganisms or reduces their growth
Anticoagulants	drugs that prevent the clotting of blood – used to stop blood clots forming or to break up blood clots
Antihistamine	a drug used to relieve the symptoms of allergies
Antiseptic	a chemical used to reduce the infectious growth of bacteria, viruses, and fungi
Antitetanus	an injection applied when a wound may be infected with tetanus (an acute and potentially fatal disease)
Appendix	a slender projection in the large intestine. Inflammation of an infected appendix is known as appendicitis
Artery	blood vessel carrying blood away from the heart
Bartholin's glands	pair of glands that open at the junction of the vagina and the vulva
Biopsy	removal of a small piece of living tissue from an organ for microscopic examination
Bladder	organ that stores urine produced by the kidneys
Blisters	swelling containing serum (a clear, yellowish fluid)
Blood pressure	pressure of blood against the walls of the main arteries; normal range varies with age
Bone marrow	soft substance inside bones
Bronchitis	inflammation of the bronchi (tubes connecting the windpipe to the lungs; also the smaller tubes within the lungs)
Calcium	metallic element essential for normal development of the body – important part of bones and teeth
Calorie	unit used to indicate energy value of foods
Cardiology	the heart
Cardiomyopathy	disease of the heart muscle
Cartilage	hard, but flexible, substance which forms part of the skeleton
Cavity	hollow enclosed area; in dentistry, a hole in a tooth
Cervical cancer	cancer of the neck (cervix) of the uterus
Chest (thorax)	part of the body cavity between the neck and the diaphragm (the midriff)
Cholesterol	fat-like substance present in the blood and most tissues, especially the nervous tissue

Circulation	movement (circuit) of blood around the body (cardio-vascular system)
Clitoris	small sensitive organ in women; part of the reproductive organs
Clot	semi-solid blood (when blood turns from a liquid into a solid)
Compress	pad of material soaked in hot or cold water
Conception	start of pregnancy when a male cell fertilises a female cell in the fallopian tube
Constipation	condition when bowels are opened infrequently or incompletely (motions are dry and hard)
Constipation	difficulty or infrequency in evacuating the bowels
D and C (dilatation and curettage)	procedure in which the lining of the uterus is scraped away
Dermatology	skin disorders
Diagnosis	process of determining a disease by considering signs and symptoms, etc
Diarrhoea	passage of frequent, more or less fluid material from the bowels, not a disease but a symptom of an underlying disorder
Diathermy	production of heat in a part of the body by means of high-frequency electric current passed from electrodes placed on the skin
Disc	rounded flattened structure such as an intervertebral disc (back bone)
Disease	disorder with recognisable signs and symptoms
Diuretic	a chemical that increases the production of urine to help the body rid itself of excess fluids
Duodenum	part of the small intestine that further digests food
Dysplasia	abnormal development of skin, bone and other tissue
Eardrum (tympanic)	the membrane at the inner end of the external tube, separating the outer and middle ears
−ectomy	removal of an organ, for example appendicectomy is removal of the appendix
Endocrinology	glands and hormones
Endometrium	mucous membrane lining the inside of the uterus
Endoscope	an instrument used for examining the inside of the body, also used for surgery
Enzyme	a protein molecule used by cells to speed up chemical processes
Epilepsy	a general term for brain disorders associated with convulsions and impaired consciousness
Eustachian tube	connects the middle ear to the pharynx
fallopian tubes	two tubes that carry the ova from from the ovaries to the uterus
Fever	increased body temperature, a symptom of disease
Flexor	a muscle that, when contracted, bends a joint or limb
Follicle	very small sac or gland in the ovary in which the ova are formed
Forensic medicine	the causes of injury and death in unexplained circumstances
Gastroenterology	digestive tract, liver, biliary tract and pancreas
General surgery	injuries, deformities or disease by operation or manipulation
Gingivitis	inflammation of the gums

Haematology	the blood
Haemoglobin	a red-pigmented protein found in red blood cells
Haemorrhoids	(or piles) distended veins usually filled with blood clots found around the anus
Haemostasis	stopping bleeding or preventing blood circulation, usually during an operation
Halitosis	bad breath
Heart attack	severe chest pain resulting from the death of part of the heart
(myocardial hormone	substance that is produced in one part of the body and is then passed into the blood stream and carried to other organs or tissues
Hydrocephalus	an accumulation of fluid inside the skull, usually resulting from an obstruction
Hydrotherapy	treatment using water, eg. baths
Hypertension	high blood pressure
Hysterectomy	surgical operation to remove the uterus
Impetigo	a skin infection that occurs predominantly in children
Incontinence	involuntary urination
Infarction/or coronary	muscle (myocardium) which follows the interruption of its blood
Influenza	(or flu) an infectious disease caused by the influenza virus
Insomnia	difficulty in getting to sleep or staying asleep
Insulin	substance that helps to control sugar loads within the body
Intensive Therapy Unit	seriously ill patients by specialist care
Labyrinth	system of cavities and ducts involved in hearing and balance
Large intestine	wide tube below the stomach where digestion of food takes place
Larynx	organ of the voice; also an air passage from the pharynx to the lungs
Ligaments	tough band of fibrous tissue that links two bones together at a joint (joint capsule)
Lymphatic system	the immune system of a body
Malignant	describing any disorder or tumour that becomes life-threatening if untreated
Manipulation	use of the hands to produce movement of bones, joints or soft tissues as part of treatment
Massage	manipulation of the soft tissue of the body
Mastoidectomy	surgical operation to remove some or all of the cells in the bone behind the ear when they have become infected
Medicine	disease or injury by drugs
Melanin	a skin pigment associated with darker skins
Membrane	thin layer of tissue surrounding part or the whole of an organ
Menopause	the end of reproductive life in women
Menopause	the end of reproductive life in women when menstruation finally stops
Menstruation	discharge of blood from the vagina on a monthly cycle
Metabolism	the sum of all the chemical and physical changes that take place within the body and enable its continued growth and functioning
Migraine	a common type of headache, felt on only one side of the body
Muscle	tissue with the power to contract – enables the body to move
Myringotomy	cut or incision of the eardrum to make an artificial opening

−natal	referring to birth, for example antenatal means before birth
Neuralgia	a disorder of the nervous system, involving sudden pain without inflammation
Neurology	the nervous system
Neurophysiology	the study of the structure and function of the nervous system
Obstetrics	pregnancy and childbirth
Oesophagus	the gullet − a muscular tube that extends from the pharynx to the stomach
Oncology	tumours
Orthopaedic	deformities caused by disease or damage to the bones and joints of the skeleton
Osteoporosis	abnormality in which bones become dense and brittle and tend to fracture; common in the elderly
Osteoporosis	abnormality in which bones become dense; a common disorder in women after the menopause
Otorhinolaryngology	ear, nose and throat (ENT)
Ovaries	glands which produce ova (egg cells) in women
Oxygen	odourless and colourless gas that is essential to most forms of life
Paediatrics	childhood ailments
Pathology	the disease process, nature and causes
Percussion	diagnostic technique for examining the chest or abdomen by tapping it with the fingers and listening to the resonance of the sound produced
Pharynx	throat
Physiotherapy	healing by exercise including the use of infrared, and ultraviolet rays, etc
Placenta	an organ that filters oxygen and food from the mother to the fetus through the umbilical cord
Plaque	flat or raised patches on the moist membrane lining tubular structures
Platelets	small disc-shaped bodies in the blood which play an important role in coagulation
Polyp	growth, usually benign (not malignant) attached to the surface from which commonly found in the nose and sinuses growing by a stalk,
Postural drainage	technique that enables a person whose lungs are clogged with sputum to drain them
Psoriasis	a common skin disease
Psychiatry	mental disorders
Radiology	disease or injury by X-Ray
Radiotherapy	(treatment by) x-rays, beta rays or gamma rays
Reconstructive surgery	damaged or deformed parts of the body by plastic surgery
Rectum	last part of the large intestine
Respiratory	breathing
Respiratory system	the organs and tissues that enable air to pass in and out of the body (lungs), ie. breathing
Resuscitation	involves maintaining the flow of blood to the body's organs until the person's heartbeat and breathing can be restarted
Rheumatism	a term for several diseases that affect joints, muscles, ligaments or tendons, such as arthritis or lumbago

Ruptured	bursting apart of an organ or tissue
Sedative	a drug used either for a calming effect or to produce sleep
Sodium	mineral element and an important part of the body – the amount of sodium in the body is controlled by the kidneys
Spina bifida	a birth defect where part of the spinal cord is left exposed
Sputum (phlegm)	mucous material released from glands in the walls of the main airways in the lungs
Stenosis	narrowing of a passage in the body
Sterile	completely free from bacteria, etc
Stroke	sudden damage to brain tissue caused by a lack of blood supply or rupture of a blood vessel; leads to weakness affecting one side of the body
Suture	a surgical stitch *or* an immovable joint
Tendon	tough cord that attaches the end of a muscle to a bone
TENS	transcutaneous electrical nerve stimulation – pain relief by the application of tiny electrical impulses to nerve endings under the skin
Therapy	treatment of disease
Thrombosis	formation of a blood clot
Thyroid	organ in the neck that produces a hormone (iodine)
Tissues	collection of cells from which the body is built
Tonsils	two glands on either side of the back of the mouth – help protect the body from infection
Toxic	poisonous
Tract	organ or collection of organs, enabling the passage of something
Trichomonas	a type of parasitic microorganism
Ulcer	an erosion or disintegration of tissues, which can be on the skin or mucous surfaces. Ulcers of the gastrointestinal tract are called peptic ulcers
Ulnar nerve	a nerve on the inner side of the arm near the elbow
Ultrasound	ultrasonic waves – sound waves of extremely high frequency that cannot be heard by the human ear
Urination	passing of water and waste products (urea) out of the body
Urology	the urinary tract
Uterus	part of the female reproductive tract where the fetus (unborn child) grows muscular passage leading to the uterus
Vagina	muscular passage leading to the uterus
Vein	blood vessel carrying blood towards the heart
Vertigo	spinning sensation but there may be a feeling that the ground is tilting – feeling of constant movement
Vessels	tubes carrying body fluid, especially blood
Vulva	the female external genitalia (reproductive organs) – two pairs of fleshy folds surrounding the opening of the vagina
Womb (uterus)	part of the female reproductive organ; where the growing foetus (unborn child) is nourished from its mother.